PRIVACY AND IDENTITY

LOCATION-BASED SERVICES

DEVELOPMENTS AND PRIVACY ISSUES

PRIVACY AND IDENTITY PROTECTION

Additional books in this series can be found on Nova's website
under the Series tab.

Additional e-books in this series can be found on Nova's website
under the e-book tab.

LOCATION-BASED SERVICES

DEVELOPMENTS AND PRIVACY ISSUES

HARVEY P. MASTERS
EDITOR

New York

For permission to use material from this book please contact us:
Telephone 631-231-7269; Fax 631-231-8175
Web Site: http://www.novapublishers.com

Additional color graphics may be available in the e-book version of this book.

Library of Congress Cataloging-in-Publication Data

ISBN: 978-1-63117-894-8

Published by Nova Science Publishers, Inc. † New York

CONTENTS

Preface   **vii**

Chapter 1   Location-Based Services: An Overview of
                  Opportunities and Other Considerations   **1**
                  Federal Communications Bureau

Chapter 2   In-Car Location-Based Services: Companies Are
                  Taking Steps to Protect Privacy, but Some Risks
                  May Not Be Clear to Consumers   **41**
                  United States Government Accountability Office

Index   **69**

PREFACE

This book addresses what selected companies that provide in-car location-based services use location data for and if they share the data, and how these companies' policies and reported practices align with industry-recommended privacy practices.

Chapter 1 - Technological innovations, notably over the past decade, facilitate the collection of substantial amounts of personally identifiable data about virtually anyone who accesses information online. The rapid pace of change in both technology and business models is fueling an active and growing debate in the United States and around the world about the appropriate use of that data. The following report focuses on one part of the discussion: Location-based services ("LBS"), mobile services that combine information about a user's physical location with online connectivity and are transforming the way Americans work and play.

Among other things, LBS let users access relevant and up-to-date information about their surroundings, inform others of their whereabouts, and get instant access to maps and traffic information for their current location. Whether used for fleet tracking or inventory management, for machine-to-machine communications, or for social networking or entertainment, LBS can create a more dynamic user experience that adds value and convenience and changes the way people transact business and organize their activities and free time.

Not surprisingly, Americans are quickly adopting LBS. As of May 2011, 28 percent of adult Americans used mobile LBS of some type. LBS are expected to deliver $700 billion in value to consumers and business users over the next decade.

The promise of LBS, however, comes with challenges and concerns. Because mobile devices have the ability—and often the technical requirement—to regularly transmit their location to a network, they also enable the creation of a precise record of a user's locations over time. This can result in the creation of a very accurate and highly personal user profile, which raises questions of how, when and by whom this information can and should be used.

In light of these developments, the staff of the Federal Communications Commission (the "FCC" or "Commission") has prepared this report on LBS. As discussed in greater detail below, drawing upon its experience in protecting consumer privacy, Commission staff believes:

- LBS have tremendous potential to provide value and foster innovation to benefit the economy and consumers;
- LBS industry players face challenges as they attempt to provide consumers with appropriate notice and choice with respect to the use of the data generated by LBS and the devices and networks that host them;
- Industry is taking steps to respond to these challenges but the degree of responsiveness varies among companies and industry segments; and
- New issues continue to emerge that need to be addressed, timely and responsively.

Consequently, in collaboration with federal partners and industry representatives, Commission staff will continue to monitor industry compliance with applicable statutory requirements and evolving industry best practices to ensure LBS evolves to meet its fullest potential while protecting the legitimate interests of consumers in safeguarding their personally identifiable information.

Chapter 2 - The prevalence of in-car communication systems provided by auto manufacturers (called telematics systems), PNDs, and smart phones has brought significant opportunities for consumers to access location- based services in their cars. As in-car location-based services have become commonplace, privacy groups and policy makers have questioned whether location data collected by companies can be used for purposes beyond the provision of services, such as by data brokers who collect information to resell the information.

GAO was asked to review this issue. This report addresses (1) what selected companies that provide in-car location-based services use location data for and if they share the data, and (2) how these companies' policies and reported practices align with industry- recommended privacy practices. GAO selected a non-generalizable sample of 10 companies. The companies were selected because they represent the largest U.S. market share or because their services are widely used. GAO examined documentation and interviewed representatives from each company regarding their privacy practices in effect in 2013 and compared those practices to industry recommended privacy practices.

In: Location-Based Services
Editor: Harvey P. Masters

ISBN: 978-1-63117-894-8
© 2014 Nova Science Publishers, Inc.

Chapter 1

LOCATION-BASED SERVICES: AN OVERVIEW OF OPPORTUNITIES AND OTHER CONSIDERATIONS[*]

Federal Communications Bureau

I. EXECUTIVE SUMMARY

Technological innovations, notably over the past decade, facilitate the collection of substantial amounts of personally identifiable data about virtually anyone who accesses information online. The rapid pace of change in both technology and business models is fueling an active and growing debate in the United States and around the world about the appropriate use of that data. The following report focuses on one part of the discussion: Location-based services ("LBS"), mobile services that combine information about a user's physical location with online connectivity and are transforming the way Americans work and play.

Among other things, LBS let users access relevant and up-to-date information about their surroundings, inform others of their whereabouts, and get instant access to maps and traffic information for their current location. Whether used for fleet tracking or inventory management, for machine-to-machine communications, or for social networking or entertainment, LBS can create a more dynamic user experience that adds value and convenience and

---

[*] This is an edited, reformatted and augmented version of a report dated May 2012.

changes the way people transact business and organize their activities and free time.

Not surprisingly, Americans are quickly adopting LBS. As of May 2011, 28 percent of adult Americans used mobile LBS of some type.[1] LBS are expected to deliver $700 billion in value to consumers and business users over the next decade.[2]

The promise of LBS, however, comes with challenges and concerns. Because mobile devices have the ability—and often the technical requirement—to regularly transmit their location to a network, they also enable the creation of a precise record of a user's locations over time. This can result in the creation of a very accurate and highly personal user profile, which raises questions of how, when and by whom this information can and should be used.

In light of these developments, the staff of the Federal Communications Commission (the "FCC" or "Commission") has prepared this report on LBS. As discussed in greater detail below, drawing upon its experience in protecting consumer privacy, Commission staff believes:

- LBS have tremendous potential to provide value and foster innovation to benefit the economy and consumers;
- LBS industry players face challenges as they attempt to provide consumers with appropriate notice and choice with respect to the use of the data generated by LBS and the devices and networks that host them;
- Industry is taking steps to respond to these challenges but the degree of responsiveness varies among companies and industry segments; and
- New issues continue to emerge that need to be addressed, timely and responsively.

Consequently, in collaboration with federal partners and industry representatives, Commission staff will continue to monitor industry compliance with applicable statutory requirements and evolving industry best practices to ensure LBS evolves to meet its fullest potential while protecting the legitimate interests of consumers in safeguarding their personally identifiable information.

II. INTRODUCTION

The FCC has decades of experience protecting consumer privacy by implementing privacy protection statutes, providing technical and policy guidance on privacy issues, and interacting with other agencies and representatives of the Executive Branch to develop a consistent approach to privacy protection. As the expert agency on communications and broadband networks, the Commission has an important role in protecting consumer privacy in the future.

Consistent with this role, on June 28, 2011, the FCC hosted a full-day workshop on LBS and the privacy issues they raise.[3] Participants included privacy policy experts as well as representatives from a cross section of companies active in enabling LBS, including technology, broadband and LBS providers and entrepreneurs. The workshop sought to raise awareness about the potential of LBS while highlighting the need to protect the basic ideals of consumer choice and privacy. At the workshop the agency gathered information from wireless carriers, application developers and business and academic leaders about trends in the development and use of LBS. Among the issues explored was a review of industry best practices for protecting personal information and what consumers should know about protecting themselves while using these services. Stakeholders recognized the importance of addressing privacy questions in order to protect basic privacy values as well as making sure consumer concerns about the use of their location information and its security do not slow adoption of innovative services or opportunities.[4]

Other agencies, including the Federal Trade Commission ("FTC") and the Department of Commerce, also have been assessing mobile privacy issues, raising consumer awareness, and encouraging proactive industry involvement to address challenges and concerns. In addition, Congress conducted several hearings that addressed location data privacy.[5] These hearings have dealt generally with the rapidly changing technology, the surge in LBS and the need to ensure the protection of the privacy rights of LBS users through the development of appropriate policy frameworks. Legislation dealing with LBS privacy issues also has been introduced.[6] There have been important industry-led efforts as well.[7]

LBS offer great potential for both business and consumers. But with that potential comes the need to better inform LBS users about privacy considerations and ensure the confidentiality and protection of their personal and proprietary information. This staff report offers an overview of the opportunities and challenges of LBS. It reviews the Commission's role in protecting consumer privacy and describes the Commission's LBS Forum, which includes an explanation of the underlying technologies. It also provides a description of LBS offerings and related privacy issues, and concludes with a discussion of other government efforts with respect to LBS.

III. THE FCC'S ROLE IN PRIVACY REGULATION AND ENFORCEMENT

The Commission's involvement in the protection of consumer privacy is rooted in the Communications Act of 1934, as amended (the "Act"), which charges the FCC with implementing a number of privacy protection provisions. Section 222 of the Act and our implementing rules, for example, require telecommunications carriers and interconnected Voice over Internet Protocol ("VoIP") providers to secure customer proprietary network information ("CPNI").[8] The FCC has adopted rules implementing Section 222 of the Act to address the handling, use, and sharing of CPNI, as well as rules to prevent pretexting, the practice by which unauthorized third parties attempt to gain access to telephone subscribers' CPNI.[9] Through rulemakings and enforcement actions, the FCC has resolved difficult issues related to its CPNI rules, including establishing minimum notice standards, determining when opt-in and opt-out choices for consumers are appropriate, adopting data sharing rules and reasonable data security measures, and requiring notification to law enforcement and consumers in the event of data breaches.[10] As a result of the Commission's actions, the Section 222 protections are sound, well understood by industry and consumers, and judicially approved.[11] Thus, the Commission has seen the number of consumer complaints related to CPNI decline steadily.[12]

Other sections of the Act require communications providers to protect personal information. Sections 338(i) and 631 establish requirements for satellite and cable television providers, respectively, for the treatment of their subscribers' personally identifiable information ("PII").[13] Specifically, these provisions require clear and conspicuous notice about collection and use of PII, limit disclosure of PII, and require cable and satellite providers to employ reasonable levels of security for their subscribers' PII.[14] In addition, Sections 338(i) and 631 contain private rights of action such that consumers have a legal remedy if their PII is improperly collected, used or disclosed.[15]

In addition to enforcing the Act's privacy provisions, the Commission has engaged in numerous initiatives to address privacy concerns. The Commission has established an internal working group comprised of experts from different bureaus and offices who meet periodically to examine privacy issues, developments in privacy laws and issues, location-based issues, and online security issues. This group also has conducted information gathering meetings on privacy issues with representatives of the cable industry, the satellite industry, telecommunications carriers, and trade associations.

Educating consumers about privacy and data security is an important priority at the Commission. The agency's Consumer and Governmental Affairs Bureau issues Consumer Alerts and makes available Factsheets addressing privacy and security issues.[16] It also devotes sections on its website to informing consumers about how to protect their privacy. In addition, the Commission's Consumer Help Center is staffed with personnel trained to answer questions from callers on several different issues including privacy concerns. The Commission created an online guide for consumers showing how to activate encryption features on wireless routers to help consumers secure their home networks and developed a Cybersecurity Tip Sheet to help small businesses understand and implement precautions to secure their networks.[17]

The Commission works collaboratively with other federal agencies, as well as consumer, educational, and other privacy groups, to educate consumers and ensure consistency across the government in protecting privacy. The FCC and the FTC have a joint task force devoted to examining privacy issues generally and location-based privacy issues specifically. The Commission also has partnered with the FTC on education efforts like Net Cetera and OnGuard Online, which offer consumers advice on how to protect their children's personal information, guard against identity theft, and avoid e-mail and phishing scams. FCC staff also participated in an interagency task force assembled by the White House Office of Science and Technology Policy with the goal of developing administration policy on commercial data privacy issues. The Small Business Administration collaborated with the Commission on small business cybersecurity initiatives. The Commission also is a member of the National Initiative for Cybersecurity Education partnership led by the Department of Commerce and has partnered with the U.S. Chamber of Commerce, the National Urban League, and others to develop and distribute privacy and cybersecurity tip sheets and other educational materials.

The Commission's collaborative efforts have extended beyond education. Working in conjunction with the FTC, the FCC adopted "Do-Not-Call" regulations under Section 227 of the Act.[18] The FCC and the FTC also collaborate on implementation of the CAN-SPAM Act,[19] with the FCC adopting rules prohibiting sending unwanted commercial email messages to wireless accounts without prior permission.[20]

In conjunction with the Department of Justice, the FCC enforces Section 705 of the Act, which restricts the unauthorized divulgence, publication, or use of certain communications.[21]

The Commission's role as an advocate and safeguard of consumer privacy was underscored by the Congressional testimony of Chairman Julius Genachowski and FCC General Counsel Austin Schlick regarding privacy issues at hearings during the summer of 2011.[22] In their testimony, both Chairman Genachowski and General Counsel Schlick discussed the three overarching goals of the Commission's approach to privacy: (1) ensuring that personal information is protected from misuse and mishandling; (2) requiring providers to be transparent about their practices; and (3) enabling consumer control and choice.[23]

In his testimony, Chairman Genachowski stressed the importance of balancing the benefits provided by technology against the dangers and challenges that technology can bring, while looking to technology to be part of the solution.[24] He encouraged industry to use its expertise to empower consumers, provide transparency and protect data.[25]

IV.

Location-based services have great potential for growth. While estimates vary,[26] most research indicates that revenues are expected to triple in the next five years.[27] Although Apple's application store has only been in operation since July of 2008, it surpassed 25 billion downloads worldwide as of March 2012.[28]

This growth trend extends to applications that rely on a user's location: 7,200 location-based applications were offered in February 2010, compared to 3,300 location-applications in July 2009.[29] In June 2011, Foursquare, the location-based social networking company, reported that it had exceeded ten million users who have "checked-in," posting their location to friends over 750 million times.[30]

LBS have facilitated the development of several types of services and applications:

- **Navigation and Travel** – Applications in this category allow a user to perform a search based in part on location, *i.e.*, to find the nearest hotel, ATM, bus stop, or particular restaurant.[31]
- **Tracking and Geosocial Networking** – Using applications in this category, users can share their location with friends, family, or strangers via online social networks. Included in this category are applications that recommend restaurants or other places of interest based on where a user's network of "friends" has checked-in, or that enables businesses to reward their customers for loyalty based on repeated visits or check-ins. Other applications in this category enable parents to track the location of their children, family and caregivers to monitor dementia patients, and pet owners to recover lost dogs. [32]
- **Gaming and Entertainment** – These applications allow users to play games on their wireless devices with friends and family, persons in their local network, or anyone online. Some location-based games track phone movement and create real-life scavenger hunts. This category also includes photography and video applications that record the GPS location tags for photos and videos or allow users to add location information to their photos.[33]
- **Retail and Real Estate** – Retail applications enable consumers to find the nearest store, provide in-store maps, check real-time inventory data, or shop from their phone, while real estate applications show houses for sale or rent or in foreclosure in a given area.[34]
- **Advertising** – Location-based advertising allows users to receive ads relevant to their current location or based on patterns of frequently visited locations. The ads generally appear within other applications or in web browser windows.[35]
- **News and Weather** – These applications provide users with weather and news targeted to their specific location.[36] Some applications provide connection to local radio or TV providers for video or audio streaming, including access to police scanners.
- **Device Management** – LBS management applications allow users to track and control their wireless devices from other sources (like a home computer) or to control other devices from their wireless devices.[37] This may include tracking, locking, or erasing a lost phone, or locating, unlocking, and starting a vehicle.
- **Public Safety** – Some LBS applications principally serve public safety functions. In addition to the San Ramon Valley California Fire

Protection District CPR application described above, Google is developing an "Amber Alert" application that would inform users in the possible vicinity of missing or abducted children.[38] Another application that has been developed by the University of Maryland enables students to alert campus security to an incident, provide its location, and stream live audio and video directly to the dispatcher.[39]

V. FCC FORUM ON LOCATION-BASED SERVICES

On June 28, 2011, the Commission, in consultation with the FTC, held a public education forum on LBS featuring representatives of telecommunications carriers, technology companies, consumer advocacy groups, and academia. The forum featured three panel discussions and several presentations on technology, applications, and policy implications of LBS. Topics included how LBS works, benefits and risks of LBS, industry and consumer best practices, and what parents should know about location tracking when their children use mobile devices.[40]

A. LBS Technologies

The forum began with a tutorial on location technology and associated data flows given by Professor Matt Blaze of the University of Pennsylvania.[41] According to Professor Blaze, there are three primary location technologies currently in use:

- *Cellular Sector/Base ID.* Cellular handsets must constantly register their presence with the nearest base station in order to establish service even when in standby mode.[42] Because the network operator has the exact location of each base station, the location of the handset can be resolved to within the coverage area. The radius covered can vary greatly, from several miles down to a city block or even an individual business or residence, depending on the cell density and network architecture. Increased resolution can be achieved by triangulating between overlapping cell sectors and is often used by providers to improve accuracy for emergency response and to monitor coverage.

- *Global Positioning System (GPS).* A substantial majority of mobile handsets, as well as an increasing number of tablets and laptops, are equipped with GPS chips that allow the devices to calculate their own position to within ten meters or less. GPS can determine location independently of other technologies, though it is often used in conjunction with them to enable a quicker location fix or where the required line-of-sight to the sky is obscured. While the location can be calculated entirely by the device, it is generally in the form of simple coordinates (*e.g.* latitude and longitude), and most mobile applications need to transmit that data to third parties in order to obtain maps or other information based on the device's location.

- *Wi-Fi.* LBS leverage the Wi-Fi technologies in handheld devices that scan their surroundings for known or open networks. Wi-Fi LBS rely on active surveys of an area to note the unique identifier and location of each Wi-Fi base station. These may include everything from hotspots in coffee shops and hotels to residential and business networks. When a Wi-Fi enabled device accesses a location service, the browser or application may send to the service the coordinates of Wi-Fi networks it currently "sees," enabling the current location to be triangulated.

As Professor Blaze noted, the technology employed in LBS is evolving rapidly and is becoming more accurate, less expensive, and faster. In addition, the specific technology employed is generally transparent to the user. Depending on the application, once a user's location has been determined, it is generally transmitted to one or more entities, including third parties with whom the user may have no established commercial relationship. Parties to whom location data may be available include the wireless carrier to which the user subscribes, the handset manufacturer, operating system developer, application developer, location service provider, advertiser or ad network, and others. According to Professor Blaze, slight shifts in an application's architecture that may adjust the amount or level of detail of personal information collected by the LBS can have profound privacy implications.[43]

B. Trends in Location Based Services

The first panel at the forum discussed current trends in LBS, including the types of LBS currently offered, potential new LBS offerings in development, and overall LBS usage trends. The panel also discussed the business and technological interactions between wireless carriers, operating system developers and application developers.[44]

The panelists first reviewed current trends in the LBS marketplace. They highlighted the continuing development of social networking applications that facilitate interaction among users by identifying their location to a network of friends. Examples of these applications offered by the panelists include Foursquare, a location-based social networking website for mobile devices that permits users to check-in to their location, and Facebook's Places, an application that allows users to voluntarily share their location to facilitate "serendipitous encounters" among a network of friends. Another trend in LBS applications noted by the panelists is reward-based applications, including applications for businesses to reward frequent customers for loyalty and user-directed reward applications that provide users with rewards for taking steps toward certain goals.

The panel also discussed the types of data needed to support these LBS applications. The panelists emphasized that the vast majority of LBS applications rely on personal information that is submitted voluntarily by consumers. For example, according to the panel, Google's Android operating system employs a "permission-based model," under which the operating system will notify the user at the time of installation that the particular application is attempting to access the user's location information and gives the user the option to share his information. In addition, the panel discussed uses of aggregate information that is not personally identifiable, for example, information about the number of mobile devices within a particular location at a given time.

These panelists also discussed the challenges posed by consumer privacy in LBS and what the industry is doing to meet those challenges. They focused on the importance of maintaining consumer privacy in order to increase trust between the consumer and the business. They also noted the sometimes conflicting goals of attaining full disclosure of privacy practices without unnecessarily impeding the user experience.

The panel ended with a discussion of whether there was any emerging consensus regarding privacy best practices for LBS. The panelists concurred that there is no "silver bullet" for privacy protections because of the vastly different LBS applications. However, panelists also agreed that companies will continue to compete in privacy innovation to try to win customers by providing superior privacy protections.

C. Company-Based Approaches to Protect Privacy

The second panel of the forum focused on company-based approaches to protecting privacy.[45] Panelists discussed measures the industry is taking to protect consumer privacy, establish industry best practices, and develop privacy-enhancing technologies. The panel also discussed the ways in which companies provide information about their privacy policies to consumers, such as the use of consumer privacy notices and the type of information typically disclosed in these notices.

The panel discussed the role of government in promoting location privacy standards. Most panelists agreed that there is a role for the Federal Government to play in developing baseline standards for privacy practices and either promoting those practices or developing baseline privacy legislation that would mandate best practices. Panelists acknowledged that because of the diverse players in the LBS business environment, some type of baseline consumer privacy legislation to establish best practice guidelines may be beneficial. Such baseline standards would be helpful in promoting a consistent approach and setting consumer expectations, and should at a minimum require transparent disclosure of companies' privacy practices. The panelists also noted, however, that given the pace of technological development, baseline privacy standards—either as recommended best practices or as the basis for legislation— should focus on widely applicable principles and not be overly specific such that they would quickly become outdated. The panel encouraged expectation-setting, principles-based legislation as preferable over legislation prescribing specific mandates or rules.

In response to the discussion of the approaches that government could encourage, the panelists discussed the concept of "privacy by design," in which privacy is considered from the earliest stages of product development. Panelists agreed that government could be an effective advocate of such an approach in any recommended, non-binding best practices. However, it was noted that while it may be fairly simple for large developers to implement such practices, it may be more difficult for smaller application developers with limited resources to incorporate a "privacy by design" approach to their product development.

Panelists also discussed various industry efforts to develop a set of best practices. Panelists agreed that the guidelines developed by CTIA–The Wireless Association ("CTIA"), a trade association representing the wireless communications industry, provide a good starting point. Those guidelines support notice and opt-in permission before allowing an application to access location data. Other organizations, such as the Future of Privacy Forum, have introduced best practice guidelines that could be broadly applied across the business environment.

Notwithstanding these industry efforts, panelists noted some deficiencies in current privacy practices for LBS. For example, privacy notices can vary from carrier to carrier, device to device and platform to platform, and some believe that more consistency with respect to privacy notices would benefit consumers by making them easier to follow and understand. In addition, there continues to be incomplete disclosure of the ways that location information is used after it is collected. While the reason some applications collect location information is intuitive to consumers, other applications collect location information for no obvious or apparent purpose. A consumer may have clear notice that an application will access and use her location information and be afforded the opportunity to opt-in to the service. However, what is done with location information after the application has it may not be at all transparent to the consumer, and the location information may be sent on to third parties without the consumer's permission. The panelists discussed some specific difficulties that are posed by the small screens and limited user interfaces on mobile devices, and discussed the struggle to find a user-friendly balance of disclosure detail and frequency.

D. Public Safety Opportunities with LBS

The forum then featured a presentation and demonstration of a smartphone application developed by the San Ramon Valley California Fire Protection District that can alert users trained in CPR when someone nearby is in need of assistance.[46] Fire Chief Richard Price discussed the development process and how the application uses a registered user's location in conjunction with existing public safety systems to greatly increase the likelihood that someone in distress will receive life-saving assistance within the critical first ten minutes of the onset of cardiac distress. He also discussed some of the non-technical issues considered in the development of the application, such as the applicability of Good Samaritan laws to users of the application and concerns around retention of the location data.

E. Consumer Education in LBS

The final panel of the forum focused on the importance of educating consumers about how to protect their personal information while utilizing LBS.[47] The panel focused in particular on the challenges of protecting children in this environment and the importance of providing information to parents about location tracking when their children use mobile devices.

The panelists discussed the importance of consumer education in this area. Both industry and company representatives on the panel agreed that consumer education efforts play a vital role in the development and expansion of LBS. In particular, panelists noted that the "privacy by design" concept of product development discussed during a prior panel contemplated education and outreach at the earliest stages of location-based product development to maximize the opportunities to increase awareness of privacy issues.[48]

The panelists also discussed the importance of educating parents and providing them with the tools to protect their children while using LBS. The panelists stressed that encouraging parents to make informed choices about sharing information requires the provision of understandable, accessible information about the implications of those choices. The panelists agreed that education efforts should focus on finding the balance between reaping the benefits of LBS while remaining aware of the potential pitfalls of such applications. This may be particularly challenging for younger generations who, panelists noted, tend to be less concerned about privacy than their parents.

The panel also discussed concerns about using LBS to market to children. Some panelists noted that marketing and advertising directly to children is among the concerns about LBS frequently mentioned by parents due to the potential to have an undue influence over children. In addition, the undesirability of such marketing and advertising made lead people to refrain from adopting and thereby benefiting from LBS. Existing laws, such as the Children's Online Privacy Protection Act ("COPPA"), attempt to regulate the marketing and advertising directed at children, and many of the government and industry education efforts, such as OnGuardOnline.gov, are directed toward teaching parents and children how to minimize receipt of location-based advertising and marketing.

The forum concluded with remarks from Peter Swire, Professor of Law at Ohio State University and former Chief Counselor for Privacy in the Office of Management and Budget during the Clinton Administration.[49] He summarized the forum by describing the tremendous potential of LBS and all the benefits that can flow from those services, while also highlighting the potential risks to consumers. Professor Swire noted that notice and choice are central to the policy discussion and consumers must be given sufficient information to make informed choices even on mobile devices with their interface limitations. Given the rapid change in the technology and marketplace, he proposed the "best practices" approach as the most effective and the most likely to lead to widespread compliance among the major players. He also noted that the role for government should be to encourage these practices and greater transparency. He reiterated that good privacy policies must address data retention and security.

VI. PRIVACY ISSUES FOR LBS

As discussed above, LBS hold great potential for spurring economic development and job creation. However, as the industry continues to develop, companies remain mindful of the associated privacy challenges. A 2009 survey of LBS users conducted by Carnegie Mellon University found that in general, consumers believe that the privacy risks of sharing their location outweigh the potential benefits of the services.[50] Thus, to facilitate increased adoption of these services and their attendant economic benefits, companies must address the key privacy issues associated with LBS.

A. Notice and Transparency

One of the most important aspects of companies' approaches to privacy is that they provide transparent notice to consumers regarding the company's privacy practices, informing the consumer as to what the company is doing with the personal information it collects. Such notice to consumers should be clear, concise, and an accurate reflection of the privacy practices of the company. Common elements of privacy notices to consumers include: categories of personal information collected and how that information will be used; opportunities and mechanisms for consumers to make choices regarding these uses, including opt-in or opt-out mechanisms for effectuating their choices; third-party access and sharing of personal information; and data minimization and data security practices. Some privacy notices also include information about a company's data retention policies for personal information and internal contact information to report concerns or problems with privacy.

Notice and transparency have long been recognized as core privacy principles. In the early stages of implementing Section 222 of the Act, the Commission recognized the importance of ensuring that customers receive "explicit notice of their CPNI rights" in order to facilitate informed decisions about carriers' use of that information.[51] The FTC has stressed greater transparency in privacy practices, calling for privacy notices to be "clearer, shorter, and more standardized" across companies.[52] The Department of Homeland Security identified transparency as its first Fair Information Privacy Principle, recognizing the importance of "transparen[cy] and provid[ing] notice to the individual regarding its collection, use, dissemination, and maintenance of personally identifiable information (PII)."[53] The Department of Commerce also recognized the value of enhanced transparency "[a]t times and in places that are most useful to enabling consumers to gain a meaningful understanding of privacy risks...."[54]

In the context of LBS, providing accurate notice and transparency of privacy practices to customers remains an important challenge.[55] As discussed at the FCC Forum, there is "limited real estate" on mobile phones, and thus they are not receptive to long, involved privacy notices.[56] A recent survey of 89 location-based applications conducted in connection with a Carnegie-Mellon study found that only 66 percent of those applications had privacy policies in place to inform users as to how personal information was treated.[57] Similarly, the Future of Privacy Forum examined the top 30 paid mobile applications across the leading operating systems as of May 2011 and found that 22 of those "lacked even a basic privacy policy."[58] In December 2010, the *Wall Street Journal* found that 45 of the 101 smart phone applications it examined did not have privacy policies to inform users of what personal information the application was collecting and using.[59]

Organizations continue to look for ways to make transparency of privacy practices for LBS consistent across services and easy for consumers to understand. Several industry associations have adopted best practices for privacy policies, including guidance on the provision of notice. CTIA highlights the importance of notice in its 2010 Best Practices and Guidelines for Location-Based Services:

> An important element of the Guidelines is notice. LBS Providers must ensure that potential users are informed about how their location information will be used, disclosed and protected so that they can make informed decisions whether or not to use the LBS, giving the user ultimate control over their location information.

The Guidelines do not dictate the form, placement, terminology used or manner of delivery of notices. LBS Providers may use written, electronic or oral notice so long as users have an opportunity to be fully informed of LBS Providers' information practices. Any notice must be provided in plain language and be understandable. It must not be misleading, and if combined with other terms or conditions, the LBS portion must be conspicuous.[60]

The Mobile Marketing Association (MMA), a trade association representing the interests of companies in the mobile marketing value chain, also highlights the importance of accurate and transparent consumer notice in its Mobile Location Based Services Marketing Whitepaper:

Notification: It is appropriate to notify the end-user about how their location information will be used, disclosed and protected so that a potential LBS user can make an informed decision whether or not to use the service or authorize the disclosure. This notice should be optimized for display within a mobile device so it is easy for end-users to navigate and read.[61]

The Direct Marketing Association (DMA), a trade association supporting multichannel direct marketing tools and techniques, highlights the importance of notice and transparency in its standards for location-based marketing in its Guidelines for Ethical Business Practice:

[M]arketers should inform individuals how location information will be used, disclosed and protected so that the individual may make an informed decision about whether or not to use the service or consent to the receipt of such communications. Location-based information must not be shared with third- party marketers unless the individual has given prior express consent for the disclosure.[62]

Individual companies have recognized the importance of notice and transparency in connection with their provision of LBS. According to Microsoft:

When the user makes a decision to allow an application to access and use location data, Microsoft provides a link to the Windows Phone Privacy Statement, which includes its own section on location services with information describing the data Windows Phone 7 collects or stores to determine location, how that data is used, and how consumers can enable or disable location-based features.[63]

Verizon Wireless notes that it "clearly discloses how it uses and collects location information in its online privacy policy and within these applications themselves."[64] Foursquare recognizes the importance of providing "transparency of our privacy practices" to users of its location-based service.[65] Several companies have separate sections of their privacy policies specifically devoted to providing transparency regarding personal information collected in connection with LBS.[66] AT&T also has recognized the importance of providing specific notice about location-based services, and amended its privacy policy in November 2010 to expand the information provided about those services.[67]

Transparency in privacy practices also has become a source of competition.[68] Companies that are able to demonstrate to consumers clear and consistent transparency in collection and use of personal information can be more competitive and, consequently, more profitable. The trust that is built between companies and their customers around transparency in privacy has become an essential precondition for building and maintaining productive customer relationships.[69]

B. Meaningful Consumer Choice

In addition to ensuring that consumers receive adequate notice of privacy practices, companies also face the challenge of ensuring consumers are afforded the opportunity to exercise meaningful choice with respect to the collection and use of their personal information. The concept of "choice" in privacy policies refers to providing the consumer with the opportunity to tell a company what it can and cannot do with their personal information. Choice can take the form of "opt-out," where the default option permits the company to use personal information in a particular way unless the consumer objects, or "opt-in," where the company cannot use personal information without the advance consent of the consumer.

In the LBS business environment, companies encounter unique challenges to ensuring that consumers have the opportunity to make meaningful choices. One issue these companies face is whether consumer choice should be opt-out or opt-in for location information, although there appears to be a developing consensus in the LBS industry that opt-in is appropriate for such sensitive information.[70] A Zogby International Survey commissioned by Common Sense Media and conducted in August 2010 found that "the vast majority of respondents say that search engines and online social networking sites should not be able to share their physical location with other companies before they have given specific authorization."[71]

Another particular challenge facing companies is minimizing interference with the user experience while concurrently offering meaningful choice to consumers. As noted at the FCC Forum, there is a "tension between granularity and simplicity"[72]—between the desire to ensure that consumers are provided the opportunity to make meaningful choices in real time regarding the use of their location-based information and the desire to ensure a seamless user experience.[73] Companies and third party intermediaries are developing creative choice mechanisms with this in mind, including utilizing uniform language that would allow consumers to make their privacy preferences known by categories or characteristics.

The timing of presenting consumers with options is a continuing issue for debate. Some organizations and entities support the concept of "just in time" choices in connection with LBS services in which the consumer is presented with a choice at the point of data collection.[74] In addition, there is some debate regarding how often an existing choice should be presented to the consumer for reconfirmation of the approved uses of location data, or whether a choice should be honored until the user affirmatively presents a different one.[75]

The wireless industry has acknowledged the importance of ensuring that consumers are afforded the opportunity to make meaningful choices regarding the collection and use of their personal information, particularly in connection with LBS. CTIA's Best Practices recognize this issue:

> LBS Providers must obtain user consent to the use or disclosure of location information before initiating an LBS (except in the circumstances described below where consent is obtained from account holders and users are informed of such use or disclosure). The form of consent may vary with the type of service or other circumstances, but LBS Providers bear the burden of establishing that consent to the use or disclosure of location information has been obtained before initiating an LBS.[76]

In addition, CTIA's Best Practices recognize that consumers should be afforded the opportunity to make choices regarding the use of their personal information whenever a company proposes a new use of that information:

> If, after having obtained consent, LBS Providers want to use location information for a new or materially different purpose not disclosed in the original notice, they must provide users with further notice and obtain consent to the new or other use.[77]

Similarly, the MMA has recognized the importance of consumer choice in facilitating the continued growth of mobile marketing:

> To allow continued growth, awareness and trust of mobile Location Based Marketing, it is important that marketers exercise great care to give consumers explicit and simple control of if, when, and how their location data will be used.[78]

Individually, companies have taken a variety of approaches to consumer choice. Apple acknowledges the importance of "provid[ing] its customers with the ability to control the location-based services capabilities of their devices."[79] As Microsoft has stated:

> Microsoft does not collect information to determine the approximate location of a device unless a user has expressly allowed an application to collect location information. Users that have allowed an application to access location data always have the option to access the location at an application level or they can disable location collection altogether for all applications by disabling the location service feature on their phone.[80]

Google states that "[o]pt-in consent and clear notice are required for collection and use of location information on Android."[81] Meaningful and understandable consumer choice is a particular issue with regard to children and their use of mobile technology. One of the most promising benefits of LBS is the ability of parents with minor children to monitor the movement of one's children,[82] but attendant to that benefit is the possibility that others may be able to exploit location-based information of children. Ensuring that children and their parents understand the choices they are making regarding children's location information, as well as all of the potential ramifications of such choices, is a critical ongoing challenge facing the LBS industry.

C. Third Party Access to Personal Information

The issue of third party access to personal information has long been at the center of the privacy debate. Third party access involves the question of what entities, other than the company to which a consumer's personal information was disclosed, have access to it. This issue is inextricably tied to the transparency and choice concepts discussed above, as an important part of companies' privacy policies involves providing notice of the third parties to whom personal information is disclosed. Frequently, consumer choice mechanisms involve informing companies of the consumer's preferences for disclosure of her personal information to third parties.

Location-based services have particular challenges regarding third party access to personal information. There are many players in the LBS business environment—including, but not limited to, the wireless carrier, the operating system, and the application developer—who may have access to consumers' personal information. As noted at the FCC Forum, while LBS initially developed as carrier-centric services, device manufacturers and application developers have been central to their evolution.[83] This development has been particularly challenging for privacy issues because while wireless carriers have been addressing privacy issues for many years, in many cases application developers have not faced these issues nor do they necessarily have a staff to provide advice and counsel on these issues.[84] Furthermore, "[o]nce an app[lication] has access to a user's data, there are usually no rules governing its disclosure, and no controls available to consumers to regain control of it."[85]

Industry groups and associations are taking steps to encourage application developers to include basic privacy protections in the development of their product. The Future of Privacy Forum, a think tank that seeks to advance responsible data practices, provides privacy resources for mobile application providers at a dedicated website, including "recommended practices developers should adopt to best protect the privacy and security of their consumers."[86] Similarly, TRUSTe, an independent provider of online privacy solutions, has announced the availability of a free sample mobile privacy policy for mobile application developers and publishers in order to encourage these entities to integrate privacy into the development of their product.[87] The GSM Association, an international organization representing the interests of approximately 800 mobile operators worldwide, also has developed a set of privacy design guidelines for mobile application developers.[88]

Companies in the LBS business environment acknowledge the privacy challenges posed by third party access to information and have addressed it in different ways. Apple's iPhone "presents users with a prompt before any application may begin collection of geolocation information."[89] According to Microsoft, with respect to phones using the Windows operating system, "[t]he location data stored on the phone is only accessed and used by Microsoft to calculate the location of a phone and provide it to user-authorized applications requesting location. The information stored on the phone is not made available to applications, other features of the phone or to third parties."[90] Google described its approach toward third party access to location information on its Android operating system:

> Google does not decide which applications can access location or other user information from the device. Instead, the Android operating system uses a permissions model in which the user is automatically informed of certain types of information an application will be able to access.
>
> The user may choose to trust the application by completing the installation or the user may choose to cancel the installation. An application can only access the device's GPS location or the device's network location if it displays a notice for this permission to the user at time of installation.[91]

Companies are also taking steps to ensure that third parties with whom they are affiliated are addressing privacy issues. For example, AT&T requires third party application developers that sell their applications through AT&T to have a privacy policy and to comply with the both CTIA and AT&T guidelines for LBS privacy.[92]

TechAmerica notes that many companies "require or encourage third party application developers to adhere to certain privacy guidelines in order to ensure consumers' privacy is protected."[93] Microsoft has developed guidelines for application developers to build privacy and data security protections into their products.[94]

However, there are limitations on companies' ability to control the privacy practices of third parties, as noted by Verizon Wireless:

> To the extent feasible, Verizon Wireless requires that its device suppliers incorporate privacy protections that give customers some control over the collection, use and sharing of location information by these third parties through features and tools available in the device's location settings menu. Since customers can download third party applications that do not have privacy protections, however, Verizon Wireless also warns customers to use discretion when using such applications.[95]

D. Data Security and Minimization

Data security is fundamental aspect of any organization's privacy architecture. Data security refers to the technical, physical, and administrative safeguards that have been put in place to protect personal information primarily from the risks of unauthorized disclosure or access.[96] Historically, the security measures that have been expected of companies are proportional to the sensitivity of the data requiring protection.

Thus, because location data is considered by consumers and industry to be particularly sensitive personal information, heightened security requirements reasonably can be expected of providers of LBS.

A related concept to data security is that of data minimization. Data minimization refers to the idea that a company will only retain personal information it actually needs and only for the amount of time that it is needed. Security vulnerabilities thus are minimized because even in the event of a security breach, the amount of data at risk has been minimized.[97] At the same time, location information can be very valuable for law enforcement investigations, which suggests a countervailing interest in retention of more information for longer periods of time.[98]

Industry groups have recognized the importance of security measures for individuals' location information. CTIA's Best Practices recommend specific safeguards for industry participants:

> LBS Providers must employ reasonable administrative, physical and/or technical safeguards to protect a user's location information from unauthorized access, alteration, destruction, use or disclosure. LBS Providers should use contractual measures when appropriate to protect the security, integrity and privacy of user location information.[99]

CTIA's Best Practices also recognize the need to limit retention and storage of location information to only what is needed:

> LBS Providers should retain user location information only as long as business needs require, and then must destroy or render unreadable such information on disposal. If it is necessary to retain location information for long-term use, where feasible, LBS Providers should convert location information to aggregate or anonymized data.[100]

Similarly, the MMA recognizes the importance of data security and data minimization:

> Security: Reasonable security measures should be used to ensure that a user's information is secure and not shared with non-affiliated third-parties. The need for effective security measures is heightened with respect to products and services targeted to children.

Data Retention: It is appropriate to limit the data retention of consumer data to as long as that data is commercially useful ensuring privacy and security.[101]

Individual companies also have recognized the importance of security issues in location- based services, while at the same time ensuring that consumers take responsibility for security matters that they can control and understand that no information security system is infallible.

For example, Gowalla's privacy policy specifies:

Gowalla uses commercially reasonable physical, managerial, and technical safeguards to preserve the integrity and security of your personal information. We cannot, however, ensure or warrant the security of any information you transmit to Gowalla and you do so at your own risk.

Once we receive your transmission of information, Gowalla makes commercially reasonable efforts to ensure the security of our systems. However, please note that this is not a guarantee that such information may not be accessed, disclosed, altered, or destroyed by breach of any of our physical, technical, or managerial safeguards.

To protect your privacy and security, we take reasonable steps (such as requesting a unique password) to verify your identity before granting you access to your account.

You are responsible for maintaining the secrecy of your unique password and account information, and for controlling access to your email communications from Gowalla, at all times.[102]

Loopt takes a similar approach to data security in its privacy policy:

Loopt uses commercially reasonable physical, managerial, and technical safeguards.

We cannot, however, ensure or warrant the security of any information that Loopt receives on your behalf to operate the Loopt Services or that you transmit to Loopt and you do so at your own risk.

We also cannot guarantee that such information may not be accessed, disclosed, altered, or destroyed by breach of any of our physical, technical, or managerial safeguards.[103]

VII. RECENT GOVERNMENT INITIATIVES

A. Federal Trade Commission

In March 2012, the FTC released its Privacy Report.[104] This report, adopted after extensive public comment, recommends adoption of a privacy framework applicable to all commercial entities that collect or use consumer data that can be reasonably linked to a specific consumer, computer, or other device, with the exception of entities that collect only non-sensitive data from fewer than 5,000 consumers per year and do not share the data with third parties.

The privacy framework is focused around three principles. First, the FTC encourages companies to adopt a "privacy by design" approach by building privacy protections into their everyday business practices. The FTC report also urges companies to implement privacy practices throughout their organizations, such as by assigning personnel to oversee privacy issues, training employees on privacy issues, and conducting privacy reviews when developing new products and services.

Second, the privacy framework advocates the principle of simplified consumer choice. Under the FTC's approach, consumer choice would not be necessary before collecting and using consumer data for practices that are consistent with the context of the transaction or a company's relationship with the consumer (e.g., product fulfillment, fraud prevention, internal operations, legal compliance), or are required or specifically authorized by law. For other data practices, consumers should be offered a choice at a time and in a context in which the consumer is making a decision about his or her data. Opt-in consent should be required before a company uses personal data in a manner materially different from that disclosed at the time of collection and for the collection of sensitive data, including location data, for certain purposes.

Third, the privacy framework recommends that companies take measures to make their data practices more transparent to consumers and provide consumers with reasonable access to the data that companies maintain about them. The FTC recommends that companies adopt clearer, shorter, and more standardized privacy notices to enable better comprehension and comparison of privacy practices. In addition, the FTC suggests that companies provide reasonable access to consumer data it maintains proportional to the sensitivity and intended use of the data. The report also recommended that stakeholders engage in outreach to educate consumers about the choices available to them.

The FTC report also contains a recommendation that stakeholders implement a universal mechanism to allow users to opt-out of online behavioral tracking. Such tracking involves developing profiles based on a user's web searches and online activity for the purpose of delivering personalized advertisements. The report endorsed the opt-out regime commonly known as "Do-Not-Track," which would give users more direct control over what data is collected about them.

In addition to its Privacy Report, the FTC has taken several recent actions specifically to address mobile privacy issues. The FTC has applied COPPA, which prohibits the collection of data from children under the age of 13 without express verifiable consent from a parent,[105] in an enforcement action against a mobile application developer for collecting and disclosing children's personal information without parental consent.[106] In February 2012, the FTC issued a report examining privacy disclosures in mobile applications targeted toward children.[107] Also in February 2012, the FTC issued warnings to marketers of six mobile applications that provide background screening applications that they may be in danger of violating the Fair Credit Reporting Act.[108] In April 2012, the FTC hosted a workshop to address issues arising in the mobile payments industry, including privacy issues.[109]

B. Department of Commerce

In February 2012, the Privacy Blueprint was published, summarizing the Administration's position on the protection of online consumer privacy and providing recommendations in several areas.[110] At the center of the Privacy Blueprint is a recommendation for the development of a Consumer Privacy Bill of Rights, implemented through private, industry-specific codes of conduct and legislation, which would set forth a baseline for consumer protection. The Consumer Privacy Bill of Rights would be formulated around seven principles: (1) individual control over what personal data companies collect and how they use it; (2) transparency about a company's privacy and security practices, including easily understandable and accessible, plain language statements about data practices; (3) respect for context, such that data practices are consistent with the context in which consumers provided the data, with more prominent notices for practices that are not inherent in the company/customer relationship; (4) security precautions and responsible handling of personal data; (5) consumers' right to access and correct personal data held about them commensurate with the scale, scope and sensitivity of the data; (6) focused collection of only as much personal data as needed to accomplish stated purposes; and (7) accountability to consumers and enforcement authorities for compliance with the Consumer Privacy Bill of Rights.

The Privacy Blueprint calls on the federal government, under the leadership of the Department of Commerce, to convene and facilitate a multi-stakeholder process to develop enforceable codes of conduct for particular markets or industry sectors with significant consumer data privacy issues. Companies in a particular industry then may choose whether to adopt a particular code of conduct, and such commitment will be enforceable by the FTC under its existing authority. As an initial step in implementing this aspect of the Privacy Blueprint, NTIA issued a request for comment on the multistakeholder process to develop consumer data privacy codes of conduct, and specifically the "substantive consumer data privacy issues that warrant the development of legally enforceable codes of conduct, as well as procedures to foster the development of these codes."[111] The Privacy Blueprint also recommends inclusion of international stakeholders in the multi-stakeholder process for the development of codes of conduct discussed above, as well as international collaboration in global privacy investigations and enforcement actions.

C. Pending Legislation

The proliferation of mobile devices and LBS and the related consumer privacy concerns has not escaped the attention of 112th Congress. There has been significant interest on the issue of privacy from both the House of Representatives and Senate, with several significant privacy and information security-related bills introduced and numerous hearings held throughout the year. Individual members of Congress also have made inquiries to government agencies on specific aspects of consumer privacy.

Several bills addressing privacy issues have been introduced in the 112th Congress. In the Senate, S. 1223, the Location Privacy Protection Act of 2011, was introduced by Senator Al Franken (D-MN) in June 2011 and referred to the Judiciary Committee. The legislation proposes requiring affirmative opt-in consent before a covered entity could collect, receive, record, obtain, or disclose location information collected by electronic communication devices.[112] S. 1535, the Personal Data Protection and Breach Accountability Act of 2011, was introduced by Senator Richard Blumenthal (D-CT). This bill would enhance criminal and civil penalties for theft of personally identifiable information, including location data, and would require notification and remedies to affected consumers.[113] S. 1535 was reported out of the Senate Judiciary Committee on September 22, 2011. S. 799, the Commercial Privacy Bill of Rights Act of 2011, was co- sponsored by Senators John Kerry (D-MA) and John McCain (R-AZ). It instructs the FTC to create a comprehensive framework requiring entities collecting personally identifiable information to implement data security measures and provide clear notice of the collectors' practices and intended purpose of the collection.[114] Under the bill's proposed framework, individuals would have the right to opt-out of any collection and opt-in would be required for certain types of sensitive data. The bill would also require that individuals have access to and the ability to correct any personal information collected. S. 799 was referred to the Senate Committee on Commerce, Science, and Transportation on April 12, 2011.

In the House of Representatives, Representative Bobby Rush (D-IL) introduced H.R. 611, the Building Effective Strategies to Promote Responsibility Accountability Choice Transparency Innovation Consumer Expectations and Safeguards ("BEST PRACTICES") Act.[115] Like S. 799, H.R. 611 instructs the FTC to develop a comprehensive framework requiring entities collecting covered personal and sensitive information to implement data security and notice practices. H.R. 611 also includes self-regulatory options for entities that meet certain FTC standards. Both S. 799 and H.R. 611 provide the FTC with authority to revise the definition of personally identifiable information. H.R. 611 extends the FTC rulemaking and enforcement authority over common carriers subject to the Communications Act, creating dual authority between the FTC and FCC with respect to privacy over common carrier networks. H.R. 611 was referred to the House Subcommittee on Commerce, Manufacturing, and Trade on February 18, 2011. On December 8, 2011 Representative Jose E. Serrano (D-NY) introduced a new bill "to require retail establishments that use mobile device tracking technology to display notices to that effect."[116] The bill, H.R. 3629, was referred to the House Committee on Energy and Commerce's Subcommittee on Commerce, Manufacturing, and Trade and instructs the FTC to enforce the Act under its unfair or deceptive trade practices authority.

Members of both the House and Senate have introduced separate "Do Not Track" legislation, which would give individuals the right to opt out of the collection, use, or sale of their online activities, including location based information. S. 913, the "Do-Not-Track Online Act of 2011,"[117] introduced by Senators Rockefeller (D-WV) and Pryor (D-AK), and H.R. 654, the "Do Not

Track Me Online Act,"[118] introduced by Representatives Speier (D-CA), Hastings (D-FL) and Filner (D-CA), would direct the FTC to develop standards for an opt-out "do not track" mechanism. Failure to do so would be considered an unfair or deceptive practice under Section 5 of the FTC Act.[119] Under both bills the covered entity would have to disclose its collection and sharing practices, including with whom the consumer information is shared. Both would also allow the FTC to exempt commonly accepted commercial practices, such as the collection of information for billing purposes. H.R. 654 was referred to the House Subcommittee on Commerce, Manufacturing and Trade and S. 913 was referred to the Senate Commerce Committee.

The "Do-Not-Track For Kids" bill, H.R. 1895, sponsored by Representatives Markey (D- MA) and Barton (R-TX), would amend COPPA to require opt-in from the parent for children under 13 in order to collect location data. H.R. 1895 was referred to the House Subcommittee on Commerce, Manufacturing, and Trade on May 23, 2011.

While privacy issues generally have resonated on Capitol Hill, specific interest has generated around the issues of data security and data breach notifications. Representative Bono- Mack (R-CA) sponsored the "Secure and Fortify Electronic Data Act," (the "SAFE Data Act"), H.R. 2577, which requires the FTC to promulgate rules requiring data security and breach notification for entities that own or possess data containing personal information.[120] H.R. 2577's data security requirements do not apply to service providers with respect to third party electronic communications, and the bill limits the FTC's ability to alter the scope of data defined as "personal information" and therefore protected under the Act. The bill was referred to the Subcommittee on Commerce, Manufacturing, and Trade on July 29, 2011.

Other data security bills in the House include the "Data Accountability and Trust Act," H.R. 1707,[121] introduced by Representative Rush (D-IL), and the "Data Accountability and Trust Act (DATA) of 2011," H.R. 1841, sponsored by Representatives Stearns (R-FL) and Matheson (R-UT).[122] Representatives Stearns and Matheson also introduced H.R. 1528, "The Consumer Privacy Protection Act of 2011,"[123] which is intended to provide consumers with comprehensive privacy protection concerning the use and sharing of their personal information, would apply to all non-governmental entities, and would give the FTC sole enforcement authority. All three bills have been referred to the House Subcommittee on Commerce, Manufacturing, and Trade.

In the Senate, S. 1207, the "Data Security and Breach Notification Act of 2011," sponsored by Senators Pryor (D-AK) and Rockefeller (D-WV), similarly requires the FTC to promulgate rules requiring data security and breach notification for entities that own or possess data containing personal information.[124] S. 1207 was referred to the Senate Commerce Committee on June 15, 2011 and no further action has occurred.

CONCLUSION

Location-based services are transforming the ways people across the country conduct business, organize their lives, and have fun. They can save time, money, and even lives. However, because of the technologies that enable them, LBS have the inherent ability to create accurate snapshots of their users' activities that can contain very personal information. As both the potential and the challenges of LBS have become more understood, the Commission, along with other federal agencies and Congress, has begun to assess ways to best ensure the LBS users enjoy all their benefits and that their confidential information is secure. Industry has also played an important role.

The Commission has a long tradition of ensuring that the privacy of consumers is protected. The Commission's consistent goals have been: ensuring that personal information is protected from misuse and mishandling, requiring providers to be transparent about their practices, and enabling consumer control and choice. This has helped inform Commission activities with respect to LBS, which have included a day-long forum on LBS benefits and challenges, close collaboration with other federal agencies and Congress, and constructive interaction with industry.

The potential of LBS to provide value and foster innovation to benefit the economy and consumers is tremendous. It is clear that there are also threats to consumers' legitimate interest in protecting their personally identifiable information, in particular from the lack of clear and consistent disclosure about how that information is being collected, safeguarded and used by location-based services. While industry is taking steps to minimize these threats, the degree of responsiveness varies, new issues continue to emerge, and LBS industry players face challenges as they attempt to provide consumers with appropriate notice and choice. Nonetheless, there is room for additional steps to be taken, particularly with respect to less established LBS providers, to ensure growing concerns are addressed as quickly and as comprehensively as possible—and at all levels of industry. Issues to consider include:

- **Consideration of Privacy Issues at Earliest Stages of Product Development.** What are the most effective means to ensure privacy considerations become an integral part of the product design and development process for all players in the LBS industry? What should consumers be told?
- **Security of data.** What are the rights, duties, and obligations of the parties that generate, aggregate, or hold LBS-related data to secure such data from unauthorized disclosure or access? Do they vary as a result of a party's relationship with the customer?
- **Timing and sufficiency of notice.** How much information should be pushed to consumers at different points in their interaction with an LBS, mobile, application or other provider and how should it be presented? Must the information be provided each time an application or service is used? Should there always be an opt out?
- **Data Minimization.** Should parties be encouraged to collect the minimal amount of data technically required to provide a location-based service and retain that data for the minimum amount of time necessary?

Engagement between government and industry will be essential to ensure there is an appropriate balance between the benefits of LBS technology and its challenges to user privacy. The Commission should continue to work closely with its federal partners and industry representatives to empower consumers, encourage transparency, and protect confidential data. In particular, the Commission should continue to monitor industry compliance with applicable statutory requirements and evolving industry best practices. Additional steps may be necessary if privacy issues are not met as effectively and comprehensively as possible or within reasonable time frames.

APPENDIX A

Commenters in WT Docket No. 11-84

American Civil Liberties Union ("ACLU"), Speech, Privacy, and Technology Project of the ACLU and the ACLU of Northern California
AT&T Inc.
Center for Democracy & Technology
Direct Marketing Association

Google Inc.
Interactive   Advertising   Bureau   Privacy   Rights   Clearinghouse
TechAmerica
The NetChoice Coalition True Position, Inc. Verizon Wireless
Wahab & Medenica LLC

APPENDIX B: AGENDA

Helping Consumers Harness the Potential of Location-Based Services

9:00 a.m.   **Welcome and Opening Remarks**
- Rick Kaplan, Chief, Wireless Telecommunications Bureau

9:05 a.m.   **An Overview of Location-Based Services and Technologies**
- Matt Blaze, Associate Professor, University of Pennsylvania

9:30 a.m.   **Panel 1: Trends in Location-Based Services** In this panel, carriers and application developers will discuss the types of Location-Based Services currently being offered, potential new Location-Based Services offerings that are in development, and general usage trends. In addition, the panel will discuss the business and technological interactions between carriers and application developers.

Moderators:
- Edward Felten, Chief Technologist, Federal Trade Commission
- John Leibovitz, Deputy Bureau Chief, Wireless Telecommunications Bureau, Federal Communications Commission

Panelists:
- Alan Chapell, Chairman of the Mobile Marketing Association's Privacy and Preferences Committee and Founder of Chapell & Associates
- Kristi Crum, Executive Director – Consumer Solutions Verizon Wireless

- Alan Davidson, Director of Public Policy for the Americas, Google Inc.
- Carter Griffin, General Partner, Updata Partners
- Tim Sparapani, Director of Public Policy, Facebook
- Brandt Squires, Consultant, Squirebend LLC (previously Director Livingsocial, Co-founder BuyYourFriendADrink. com)
- Jon Steinback, Director of Marketing, Foursquare Labs, Inc.

11:00 a.m. Break

11:15 a.m. Panel 2: Company-Based Approaches to Protect Privacy
Panelists will discuss measures the industry is taking to protect consumer privacy, establish industry best practices, and develop privacy-enhancing technologies. The panel will discuss the ways in which companies provide information about their privacy policies to consumers, such as the usage of consumer privacy notices and the type of information typically disclosed in these notices.

Moderators:
- Charles Mathias, Assistant Chief, Wireless Telecommunications Bureau
- Douglas Sicker, Chief Technologist, Federal Communications Commission

Panelists:
- Justin Brookman, Director, Project on Consumer Privacy, Center for Democracy and Technology
- Maureen Cooney, Deputy Chief Privacy Officer, Director of Office of Privacy, Sprint Nextel
- Lorrie Cranor, Associate Professor, Computer Science and Engineering and Public Policy, Carnegie Mellon University
- Ted Morgan, Founder and CEO, Skyhook Wireless
- Patti Poss, Counsel to the Director of the Bureau of Consumer Protection, Federal Trade Commission
- Scott Taylor, Chief Privacy Officer, Hewlett Packard

12:45 p.m. Break

1:15 p.m. Lunch Presentation by Chief Richard Price, San Ramon CA Fire Protection District

1:45 p.m.   **Panel 3: Protecting Your Privacy – What Consumers and Parents Should Know**
This panel will provide an overview of steps consumers can take now to protect their privacy when using Location-Based Services. The panel will provide consumer DOs and DON'Ts, and provide information on what parents should know about location tracking when their children use mobile devices.
Moderators:
- Joel Gurin, Chief, Consumer and Governmental Affairs Bureau
- Jennifer Tatel, Associate General Counsel, Office of General Counsel

Panelists:
- Michael Altschul, General Counsel, CTIA-The Wireless Association®
- Dr. Edward G. Amoroso, Senior Vice President and Chief Security Officer, AT&T Services, Inc.
- Stephen Balkam, CEO, Family Online Safety Institute
- Brendon Lynch, Chief Privacy Officer, Microsoft
- Alan Simpson, Vice President of Policy, Common Sense Media
- Nat Wood, Assistant Director, Division of Consumer and Business Education, Bureau of Consumer Protection, Federal Trade Commission

3:00 p.m.   **Closing Remarks**
- Peter Swire, C. William O'Neill Professor of Law, Moritz College of Law of the Ohio State University

3:15 pm   **Adjourn**

End Notes

[1] McKinsey Global Inst., *Big data: The next frontier for innovation, competition, and productivity* 85 (2011), *available at* http://www.mckinsey.com/mgi/publications/big_data/pdfs/ MGI_ big_data_full_report.pdf.

[2] *Id.*

[3] *See FCC Staff to Host Forum Aimed at Helping Consumers Navigate Location-Based Services,* Public Notice, 26 FCC Rcd 6757 (2011).

[4] *See* App. B (Agenda for FCC Forum); Section V, *infra* (discussing the FCC forum).

[5] *See, e.g., Internet Privacy: The Views of the FTC, the FCC and NTIA: Hearing Before the Subcomm. on Commerce, Manufacturing, and Trade and the Subcomm. on Communications and Technology of the H. Committee on Energy and Commerce,* 112th Cong. (July 14, 2011), http://energycommerce.house.gov/hearings/hearingdetail.aspx?newsID=8769; *Protecting Mobile Privacy: Your Smartphones, Tablets, Cell Phones and Your Privacy: Hearing Before the Subcomm. on Privacy, Technology and the Law of the S. Comm. on the Judiciary,* 112th Cong. (May 10, 2011), http://www.judiciary.senate.gov/hearings/ hearing.cfm?id=e655f9e2809e5476862f735da16bd1e7; *ECPA Reform and the Revolution in Location Based Technologies and Services: Hearing Before the Subcomm. on the Constitution , Civil Rights, and Civil Liberties of the H. Comm. on the Judiciary,* 111th Cong. (June 24, 2010), http://judiciary.house.gov/hearings/printers/111th/111-109_57082. PDF; *The Collection and Use of Location Information for Commercial Purposes: Hearing Before the Subcomm. on Commerce, Trade and Consumer Protection and the Subcomm. on Communications, Technology, and the Internet of the H. Comm. on Energy and Commerce,* 111th Cong. (Feb. 24, 2010), http://democrats.energycommerce.house.gov/index.php?q= hearing/the-collection-and-use-of- location-information-for-commercial-purposes.

[6] *See* Section VII.C., *infra.*

[7] *See* Section VI, *infra.*

[8] 47 U.S.C. § 222. CPNI includes "information that relates to the quantity, technical configuration, type, destination, location, and amount of use of a telecommunications service subscribed to by a customer of a telecommunications service, and that is made available to the carrier solely by virtue of the carrier-customer relationship" and information contained in customers' telephone bills except for subscriber list information. *Id.* § 222(h)(1).

[9] 47 C.F.R. § 64.2001 – 64.2011.

[10] *See, e.g., Implementation of the Telecommunications Act of 1996: Telecommunications Carriers' Use of Customer Proprietary Network Information and Other Customer Information,* Third Report and Order and Third Notice of Proposed Rulemaking, 17 FCC Rcd 14860 (2002).

[11] *See, e.g., NCTA v. FCC,* 555 F.3d 996 (D.C. Cir. 2009).

[12] *Privacy and Data Security: Protecting Consumers in the Modern World: Hearing Before the S. Comm. on Commerce, Science, & Transportation,* 112th Cong. (June 29, 2011) (statement of Austin C. Schlick, General Counsel, Federal Communications Commission), http:// commerce.senate.gov/public/?a=Files.Serve&File_id=8380ddf6-cdd7-4ca9-8f2d-ad511691b5a3.

[13] 47 U.S.C. §§ 338(i), 551. "Personally identifiable information" is not defined in the statute, but can be assumed to include "all individually identifiable information collected by a cable operator over a cable system regarding its subscribers." H.R. Rep. No. 934, 98th Cong., 2d Sess. (1984).

[14] 47 U.S.C. §§ 338(i), 551.

[15] *Id.* at §§ 338(i)(7), 551(f).

[16] *See* http://www.fcc.gov/encyclopedia/consumer-publications-library#Privacy.

[17] *See* FCC Consumer Tip Sheet, "Wi-Fi Networks and Consumer Privacy" (Apr. 17, 2012), *available at* http://transition.fcc.gov/Daily_Releases/Daily_Business/2012/db0417/DOC-313634A1.pdf; *see also* http://www.fcc.gov/cyberforsmallbiz (setting forth practical cybersecurity tips for small businesses).

[18] 47 U.S.C. § 227; 47 C.F.R. § 64.1200.

[19] Controlling the Assault of Non-Solicited Pornography and Marketing Act of 2003, Pub. L. No. 108-187, 117 Stat. 2699 (2003), codified at 15 U.S.C. §§ 7701-7713, 18 U.S.C. § 1037 and 28 U.S.C. § 994.

[20] 47 C.F.R. § 64.3100.

[21] 47 U.S.C. § 605.

[22] *Internet Privacy: The Views of the FTC, the FCC and NTIA: Hearing Before the Subcomm. on Commerce, Manufacturing, and Trade and the Subcomm. on Communications and Technology of the H. Committee on Energy and Commerce*, 112th Cong. (July 14, 2011) (statement of Julius Genachowski); *Privacy and Data Security: Protecting Consumers in the Modern World: Hearing Before the S. Comm. on Commerce, Science, & Transportation*, 112th Cong. (June 29, 2011) (statement of Austin C. Schlick).

[23] *Id.*

[24] *Internet Privacy: The Views of the FTC, the FCC and NTIA: Hearing Before the Subcomm. on Commerce, Manufacturing, and Trade and the Subcomm. on Communications and Technology of the H. Committee on Energy and Commerce*, 112th Cong. (July 14, 2011) (statement of Julius Genachowski).

[25] *Id.*

[26] Variations in estimates may result from different definitions of "location-based services."

[27] *See, e.g.*, Pyramid Research, Research Report, *Location-Based Services, Market Forecast, 2011-2015* (May 2011) (estimating $2.8 billion in revenues for location-based services in 2010, with growth projected to $10.3 billion in 2015), *available at* http://www. pyramidresearch.com/store/Report-Location-Based-Services.htm; Press Release, ABI Research, *Global Location-Based Platform and Infrastructure Revenues to Reach $1.8 Billion by 2015* (Mar. 15, 2010) (estimating revenues of $560 million in 2010 and $1.8 billion in 2015), *available at* http://www.abiresearch.com/press/3393-Global+Location-Based+Platform+and+Infrastructure+Revenues+to+Reach+%241.8+Billion+by+2015; Press Release, *Mobile Location-Based Services Market to exceed $12bn by 2014 driven by Increased Apps Store Usage, Smartphone Adoption and New Hybrid Positioning Technologies, According to Juniper Research* (Feb. 2010), *available at* http://www. juniperresearch.com/press-releases.php?category=2&pg=4); *see also* Pew Internet & American Life Project, *28% of American adults use mobile and social location-based services* (Sept. 2011), *available at* http://www.pewinternet.org/Reports/2011/ location.aspx.

[28] *See* Joanna Stern, *25 Billion Apps Downloaded From the Apple App Store*, ABC News (Mar. 5, 2012), *available at* http://abcnews.go.com/blogs/technology/2012/03/25-billion-apps-downloaded-from-the-apple-app-store/.

[29] Skyhook Wireless, *Location Aware App Report: Review of location-aware apps from the iPhone, Blackberry, and Android App Stores* (Feb. 2010).

[30] Remarks of Jon Steinback, Director of Marketing, Foursquare Labs, Inc., at FCC Forum.

[31] Examples of navigation and travel applications include WHERE, Yelp, Zagat, MapQuest 4 Mobile, Google Places, Yellow Pages Mobile, NextBus, OpenTable, and Star Walk.

[32] Examples of tracking and social location "check-in" applications include FourSquare, Loopt, Family Locator, Adient, Tagg, FindFriends, Gowalla, Facebook Places, Twitter, and Yelp.

[33] Examples of gaming and entertainment applications include Scrabble, Tourality, iPhone Camera, Flickr, and Geocaching.

[34] Examples of retail and real estate applications include Google Shopper, Target, Home Depot, HUD Homes, and Zillow Real Estate Search.

[35] Examples of advertising applications include WHERE Ads, SkyHook, go2 Media, and Smaato.

[36] Examples of news and weather applications include The Weather Channel, Weather HD, USA Today, NPR News, Stitcher Radio, ABC News, and Scanner911.

[37] Examples of device management applications include Find My iPhone, Lookout, OnStar MyLink, and myChevrolet.

[38] Remarks of Alan Davidson, Director of Public Policy for the Americas, Google Inc., at FCC Forum.

[39] *See* http://www.emergencymgmt.com/safety/Smartphone-Application-V911-Maryland.html.

[40] *See* App. B.

[41] *See* Presentation of Matt Blaze, Univ. of Pennsylvania, *Technology and Privacy in Mobile Location Services*, *available at* http://transition.fcc.gov/presentations/06282011/matt-blaze.pdf.

[42] The implication of this network requirement is that consumers who believe they have disabled all location tracking on their mobile device may nevertheless still be sharing some location information necessary to provide service. See infra n.79.

[43] For another useful overview of the technology behind LBS, see also *Protecting Mobile Privacy: Your Smartphones, Tablets, Cell Phones and Your Privacy: Hearing Before the Subcomm. on Privacy, Technology and the Law of the S. Comm. On the Judiciary*, 112th Cong. (May 10, 2011) (statement of Askan Soltani), *available at* http://www.judiciary. senate.gov/pdf/11-5-10%20Soltani%20Testimony%20-%20Revised.pdf ("Soltani Testimony").

[44] The participants on the first panel were Alan Chapell, Chairman of the Mobile Marketing Association's Privacy and Preferences Committee and Founder of Chapell & Associates, Kristi Crum, Executive Director – Consumer Solutions, Verizon Wireless, Alan Davidson, Director of Public Policy for the Americas, Google Inc., Carter Griffin, General Partner, Updata Partners, Tim Sparapani, Director of Public Policy, Facebook, Brandt Squires, Consultant, Squirebend LLC (previously Director Livingsocial, Co-founder BuyYourFriendADrink.com), and Jon Steinback, Director of Marketing, Foursquare Labs, Inc.

[45] The participants on the second panel were Justin Brookman, Director, Project on Consumer Privacy, Center for Democracy and Technology , Maureen Cooney, Deputy Chief Privacy Officer, Director of Office of Privacy, Sprint Nextel, Lorrie Cranor, Associate Professor, Computer Science and Engineering and Public Policy, Carnegie Mellon University, Ted Morgan, Founder and CEO, Skyhook Wireless, Patti Poss, Counsel to the Director of the Bureau of Consumer Protection, Federal Trade Commission, and Scott Taylor, Chief Privacy Officer, Hewlett Packard.

[46] http://firedepartment.mobi.

[47] The participants on the final panel were Michael Altschul, General Counsel, CTIA-The Wireless Association, Edward G. Amoroso, Senior Vice President and Chief Security Officer, AT&T Services, Inc., Stephen Balkam, CEO, Family Online Safety Institute, Brendon Lynch, Chief Privacy Officer, Microsoft, Alan Simpson, Vice President of Policy, Common Sense Media, and Nat Wood, Assistant Director, Division of Consumer and Business Education, Bureau of Consumer Protection, Federal Trade Commission.

[48] *See supra* at 15.

[49] *See* Presentation of Peter Swire, Ohio State Univ., *Wrap Up on Privacy and Location Based Services, available at* http://apps.fcc.gov/ecfs/document/view?id=7021690869.

[50] *See* Janice Y. Tsai, Patrick Gage Kelley, Lorrie Faith Cranor, Norman Sadeh, "Location-Sharing Technologies: Privacy Risks and Controls," Carnegie Mellon University at 17 (Feb. 2010).

[51] *See Implementation of the Telecommunications Act of 1996*, Second Report and Order and Further Notice of Proposed Rulemaking, 13 FCC Rcd 8061 (2002).

[52] "Protecting Consumer Privacy in an Era of Rapid Change: Recommendations for Business and Policy Makers," FTC Privacy Report at 60 (Mar. 2012), *available at* http://ftc.gov/os/2012/ 03/120326privacyreport.pdf ("FTC Privacy Report").

[53] *See* "Privacy Policy Guidance Memorandum," Dept. of Homeland Security, Memorandum No. 2008-01 at 3 (Dec. 29, 2008), *available at* http://www.dhs.gov/xlibrary/assets/privacy/ privacy_policyguide_2008-01.pdf.

[54] "Commercial Data Privacy in a Networked World: A Framework for Protecting Privacy and Promoting Innovation in the Global Economy," Dept. of Commerce Internet Policy Task Force at 14 (Feb. 2012) *available at* http://www. whitehouse.gov/sites/default/files/privacy-final.pdf ("Privacy Blueprint").

[55] Ginger Myles, Adrian Friday and Nigel Davies, "Preserving Privacy in Environments with Location-Based Applications," Pervasive Computing, IEEE Computing Society at 56 (January- March 2003) ("An important first step in protecting users' location privacy is notifying them of requests for this information.").

[56] Remarks of Peter Swire, C. William O'Neill Professor of Law, Moritz College of Law of the Ohio State University, at FCC Forum. A recent FTC workshop on mobile payments featured a session addressing the unique challenges of privacy notices on mobile devices. *See* "Paper, Plastic... or Mobile? An FTC Workshop on Mobile Payments" (Apr. 26, 2012), *available at* http://www.ftc.gov/bcp/workshops/mobilepayments/.

[57] *See supra* n.50 at 8.

[58] http://www.futureofprivacy.org/2011/05/12/fpf-finds-nearly-three-quarters-of-most- download ed-mobile-apps-lack-a-privacy-policy/.

[59] Scott Thurm and Yukari Iwatani Kane, "Your Apps Are Watching You," *Wall Street Journal* (Dec. 17, 2010), *available at* http://online.wsj.com/article/SB10001424052748704694004 576020083703574602.html.

[60] Best Practices and Guidelines for Location-Based Services, CTIA-The Wireless Association, at 3 (Mar. 23, 2010), *available at* http://www.ctia.org/business_resources/wic/index.cfm/ AID/11300 ("CTIA Best Practices").

[61] Mobile Location Based Services Marketing Whitepaper, Mobile Marketing Association, at 17 (Oct. 2011), *available at* http://www.mmaglobal.com/MobileLBSWhitepaper.pdf ("MMA White Paper").

[62] Guidelines for Ethical Business Practices, Direct Marketing Association, at 42 (May 2011), *available at* http://www.dmaresponsibility.org/Guidelines/ ("DMA Guidelines").

[63] *See* Letter from Andy Lees, President, Microsoft Mobile Communications Business, to The Honorable Fred Upton, U.S. House of Representatives (May 9, 2011).

[64] Comments of Verizon Wireless, WT Docket No. 11-84, at 2 (July 8, 2011).

[65] *See* Foursquare Labs, Inc. Privacy Policy (Jan. 12, 2011), *available at* https://foursquare.com/ legal/privacy.

[66] *See, e.g.,* Apple Inc. Privacy Policy (Oct. 21, 2011), *available at* http://www.apple.com/ privacy/; Loopt, Inc. Privacy Notice (Oct. 15, 2009), *available at* https://app.loopt.com/ loopt/privacyNotice.aspx.

[67] *See* Comments of AT&T Inc., WT Docket No. 11-84, at 5 (July 8, 2011).

[68] *See* Privacy Blueprint at 14 (promoting greater consistency among privacy notices to make companies' privacy practices "a more salient point of competition among different products and services").

[69] Remarks of Brendon Lynch, Chief Privacy Officer, Microsoft Corp., at FCC Forum (identifying privacy as "core to creating trust with our customer and core to our business success").

[70] Remarks of Peter Swire, C. William O'Neill Professor of Law, Moritz College of Law of the Ohio State University, at FCC Forum ("there is a broad sense that opt in is the way to go"); *see also* Comments of the Center for Democracy and Technology, WT Docket No. 11-84 (July 8, 2011) (calling on the FCC to confirm that "in most cases, precise geolocation data should only be collected and/or shared with the informed, affirmative consent of the person whose information is being collected and/or shared"); DMA Guidelines at 41 ("Marketers should obtain prior express consent from existing and prospective customers before sending mobile marketing to a wireless device."); FTC Privacy Report at 58-59. *But see* Letter from Peter Davidson, Senior Vice President, Federal Government Relations, Verizon, to The Honorable Joe Barton, U.S. House of Representatives, at 4 (Oct. 17, 2011) (discussing use of an opt-out mechanism for new location- based targeted marketing service).

[71] *See* Memorandum from Zogby International to Common Sense Media (Aug. 24, 2010), *available at* http://www.privacylives.com/wp-content/uploads/2010/10/Final-CSM-adults-topline-8-24-10-Updated-EMBARGO.pdf; *see also* Remarks of Carter Griffin, General Partner, Updata Partners, at FCC Forum (noting that consumers want to have "very tight control over publishing location" information).

[72] Remarks of Tim Sparapani, Director of Public Policy, Facebook, at FCC Forum.

[73] *See* Ginger Myles, Adrian Friday and Nigel Davies, "Preserving Privacy in Environments with Location-Based Applications," Pervasive Computing, IEEE Computing Society, at 56 (Jan.-

Mar. 2003) (noting the conflicting requirements of "the need for users to control their location privacy and the need to minimize the demands made of users").

[74] *See, e.g.,* TRUSTe Privacy Program Requirements, *available at* http://www.truste.com/ privacy- program-requirements/program-requirements.

[75] *See, e.g.,* Remarks of Peter Swire, C. William O'Neill Professor of Law, Moritz College of Law of the Ohio State University, at FCC Forum (discussing the "random act of kindness" that suggests presenting individuals with the opportunity to review their choices on a periodic basis).

[76] CTIA Best Practices at 5.

[77] *Id.* at 3.

[78] MMA White Paper at 4.

[79] *See* Letter from Bruce Sewell, Apple General Counsel and Senior Vice President, Legal and Government Affairs, to The Honorable Edward J. Markey, U.S. House of Representatives (July 12, 2010). *But see* Soltani Testimony, *supra* n.43, at 5-7 (discussing continued tracking and reporting of location data even though LBS on the device have been disabled).

[80] *See* Letter from Andy Lees, President, Microsoft Mobile Communications Business, to The Honorable Fred Upton, U.S. House of Representatives (May 9, 2011).

[81] Google Inc. *ex parte,* WT Docket No. 11-84 (July 8, 2011).

[82] *See supra* n.50 at 15.

[83] Remarks of Michael Altschul, General Counsel, CTIA, at FCC Forum; *see also* Comments of AT&T Inc., WT Docket No. 11-84, at 3 (July 8, 2011) ("Third-party applications and services often determine user location without any involvement by wireless carriers.").

[84] *But see* Remarks of Peter Swire, C. William O'Neill Professor of Law, Moritz College of Law of the Ohio State University, at FCC Forum (noting that application developers that fall into this category remain minor players in this industry at this time, and that the larger players with large databases of sensitive personal information, including location information, have compliance staffs and familiarity with privacy issues).

[85] Comments of the Center for Democracy and Technology, WT Docket No. 11-84 (July 8, 2011).

[86] Future of Privacy Forum Application Developer Responsible Data Use Project, *available at* http://www.applicationprivacy.org/. *See also* Remarks of Michael Altschul, General Counsel, CTIA, at FCC Forum (discussing the development of a web interface for use by application developers to identify privacy issues).

[87] *See* Press Release, "TRUSTe Extends Leadership Role in Mobile Privacy With Introduction of Free Privacy Policies for Mobile Applications" (Nov. 2, 2011), *available at* http://www.truste.com/about_TRUSTe/press-room/news_truste_free_privacy_policies_for_ mobile_applications.

[88] Privacy Design Guidelines for Mobile Application Development, GSM Association (Feb. 2012), *available at* http://www.gsma.com/documents/privacy-design-guidelines-for-mobile-application-development/20008.

[89] Comments of The NetChoice Coalition, WT Docket No. 11-84, at 2 (July 8, 2011).

[90] *See* Letter from Andy Lees, President, Microsoft Mobile Communications Business, to The Honorable Fred Upton, U.S. House of Representatives (May 9, 2011).

[91] *See Consumer Privacy and Protection in the Mobile Marketplace: Hearing Before the Subcomm. on Consumer Protection, Product Safety, and Insurance of the S. Comm. on Commerce, Science and Transportation,* 112th Cong. (May 19, 2011) (statement of Alan Davidson, Director of Public Policy for the Americas, Google Inc., at 6-7).

[92] Comments of AT&T Inc., WT Docket No. 11-84, at 5 (July 8, 2011).

[93] Comments of TechAmerica, WT Docket No. 11-84, at 4 (July 8, 2011).

[94] *See* Steve Lipner, Michael Howard, "The Trustworthy Computing Security Development Lifecycle," Microsoft Corporation (March 2005), *available at* http://msdn.microsoft.com/ en- us/library/ms995349.

[95] Comments of Verizon Wireless, WT Docket No. 11-84, at n.5 (July 8, 2011).

[96] *See also* Directive 95/46/EC of the European Parliament and of the Council of 24 October 1995 on the protection of individuals with regard to the processing of personal data and on the free movement of such data, Article 17, para. 1 (data security refers broadly to the protection of personal data "against accidental or unlawful destruction or accidental loss, alteration, unauthorized disclosure or access, in particular where the processing involves the transmission of data over a network, and against all other unlawful forms of processing").

[97] Remarks of Peter Swire, C. William O'Neill Professor of Law, Moritz College of Law of the Ohio State University, at FCC Forum ("the privacy risk can be reduced a lot if there is a limit on the time that location is kept in identifiable form").

[98] *See, e.g., ECPA Reform and the Revolution in Location Based Technologies and Services: Hearing Before the Subcomm. on the Constitution, Civil Rights and Civil Liberties of the H. Comm. on the Judiciary*, 111th Cong. (June 24, 2010) (written testimony of Richard Littlehale, Assistant Special Agent in Charge, Technical Services Unit, Tennessee Bureau of Investigation).

[99] CTIA Best Practices at 7.

[100] *Id.*

[101] MMA White Paper at 17.

[102] Privacy Policy of Gowalla, Inc., *available at* http://gowalla.com/privacy.

[103] Privacy Notice of Loopt, Inc. (Oct. 15, 2009), *available at* https://app.loopt.com/loopt/ privacyNotice.aspx.

[104] *See supra* n.52.

[105] 15 U.S.C. §§ 6501–6506. The FTC has proposed revisions to its rules implementing COPPA, including clarifying that COPPA applies to mobile devices. *See* 76 Fed. Reg. 59804 (Sept. 27, 2011).

[106] *See U.S. v. W3 Innovations, LLC*, FTC File No. 102 3251, Case No. CV-11-03958-PSG (N.D. Ca. filed Sept. 8, 2011), *available at* http://www.ftc.gov/opa/2011/08/w3mobileapps.shtm.

[107] *See Mobile Apps for Kids: Current Privacy Disclosures are Disappointing*, FTC Staff Report (Feb. 2012), *available at* http://www.ftc.gov/os/2012/02/120216mobile_apps_kids.pdf.

[108] *See* Press Release, *FTC Warns Marketers That Mobile Apps May Violate Fair Credit Reporting Act* (Feb.7, 2012), *available at* http://ftc.gov/opa/2012/02/mobileapps.shtm.

[109] *See supra* n.56.

[110] *See supra* n.54.

[111] 77 Fed. Reg. 13098 (Mar. 5, 2012).

[112] Location Privacy Protection Act of 2011, S. 1223, 112th Cong. (2011).

[113] Personal Data Protection and Breach Accountability Act of 2011, S. 1535, 112th Cong. (2011).

[114] Commercial Privacy Bill of Rights Act of 2011, S. 799, 112th Cong. (2011).

[115] BEST PRACTICES Act, H.R. 611, 112th Cong. (2011).

[116] H.R. 3629, 112th Cong. (2011).

[117] Do-Not-Track Online Act of 2011, S. 913, 112th Cong. (2011).

[118] Do Not Track Me Online Act, H.R. 654, 112th Cong. (2011).

[119] 15 U.S.C. § 45.

[120] The SAFE Data Act, H.R. 2577, 112th Cong. (2011).

[121] Data Accountability and Trust Act, H.R. 1707, 112th Cong. (2011).

[122] Data Accountability and Trust Act (DATA) of 2011, H.R. 1841, 112th Cong. (2011).

[123] The Consumer Privacy Protection Act of 2011, H.R. 1528, 112th Cong. (2011).

[124] Data Security and Breach Notification Act of 2011, S. 1207, 112th Cong. (2011).

In: Location-Based Services
Editor: Harvey P. Masters

ISBN: 978-1-63117-894-8
© 2014 Nova Science Publishers, Inc.

Chapter 2

IN-CAR LOCATION-BASED SERVICES: COMPANIES ARE TAKING STEPS TO PROTECT PRIVACY, BUT SOME RISKS MAY NOT BE CLEAR TO CONSUMERS*

United States Government Accountability Office

WHY GAO DID THIS STUDY

The prevalence of in-car communication systems provided by auto manufacturers (called telematics systems), PNDs, and smart phones has brought significant opportunities for consumers to access location- based services in their cars. As in-car location-based services have become commonplace, privacy groups and policy makers have questioned whether location data collected by companies can be used for purposes beyond the provision of services, such as by data brokers who collect information to resell the information.

GAO was asked to review this issue. This report addresses (1) what selected companies that provide in-car location-based services use location data for and if they share the data, and (2) how these companies' policies and reported practices align with industry- recommended privacy practices. GAO

---

* This is an edited, reformatted and augmented version of the United States Government Accountability Office publication, GAO-14-81, dated December 2013.

selected a non-generalizable sample of 10 companies. The companies were selected because they represent the largest U.S. market share or because their services are widely used. GAO examined documentation and interviewed representatives from each company regarding their privacy practices in effect in 2013 and compared those practices to industry recommended privacy practices.

WHAT GAO RECOMMENDS

Since this report examines private companies' use of location data, GAO is not making recommendations to federal agencies. The Department of Commerce, Federal Trade Commission, and the selected companies provided technical comments, which GAO incorporated as appropriate.

WHAT GAO FOUND

Representatives from all 10 selected companies—auto manufacturers, portable navigation device (PND) companies, and developers of map and navigation applications for mobile devices—said they collect location data to provide consumers with location-based services. For example, companies collect location data to provide turn-by-turn directions. Nine companies share location data with third-party companies, such as traffic information providers, to provide services to consumers. Representatives from two companies said they share data where personally identifiable information has been removed (de-identified data) for purposes beyond providing services (e.g., for research), although such purposes are not always disclosed to consumers. All company representatives said that they do not share personally identifiable location data with or sell such data to marketing companies or data brokers.

All 10 selected companies have taken steps consistent with some, but not all, industry-recommended privacy practices. In addition, the companies' privacy practices were, in certain instances, unclear, which could make it difficult for consumers to understand the privacy risks that may exist.

- *Disclosures*: Consistent with recommended practices, all selected companies disclose that they collect and share location data. However, inconsistent with recommended practices, nine companies' disclosures provide reasons for collecting data that are broadly worded (e.g., the stated reasons for collecting location data were not exhaustive), and five companies' disclosures do not describe the purposes for sharing de-identified location data. Without clear disclosures, risks increase that data may be collected or shared for purposes that the consumer is not expecting or might not have agreed to.

- *Consent and controls*: Consistent with recommended practices, all selected companies obtain consumer consent to collect location data and obtain this consent in various ways. In addition, all companies offered consumers some controls over location data collection. However, if companies retained data, they did not allow consumers to request that their data be deleted, which is a recommended practice. Without the ability to delete data, consumers are unable to prevent the use or retention of their data, should they wish to do so.

- *Safeguards and retention*: All selected companies take steps to safeguard location data—a recommended practice—but use different de-identification methods that affect the extent to which consumers may be re-identified and exposed to privacy risks. Also, there is wide variation in how long companies retain vehicle-specific or personally identifiable location data. To the extent that a company's de-identification methods allow a consumer to be identified or that identifiable data are retained, risks increase that location data may be used in ways consumers did not intend or may be vulnerable to unauthorized access.

- *Accountability*: All selected companies disclose to consumers or take steps to protect location data that they share with third parties; such efforts are consistent with recommended practices. However, inconsistent with recommended practices, none of the selected companies disclose to consumers how they hold themselves and their employees accountable. The companies told GAO that internal company policies serve this function.

ABBREVIATIONS

Communications Act	Communications Act of 1934
CPNI	customer proprietary network information
ECPA	Electronic Communications Privacy Act of 1986

FIPP	Fair Information Practice Principles
FTC	Federal Trade Commission
GPS	Global Positioning Satellite
NHTSA	National Highway Transportation Safety Administration
NTIA	National Telecommunications and Information Administration
PND	portable navigation device
OECD	Organisation for Economic Co-operation and Development
VIN	vehicle identification number

December 6, 2013

The Honorable Al Franken
Chairman
Subcommittee on Privacy,
Technology and the Law
Committee on the Judiciary
United States Senate

Dear Mr. Chairman:

The prevalence of in-car communication systems (called "telematics"),[1] as well as portable navigation devices (PND) and smart phones, has brought significant opportunities for consumers to access location-based services in their cars.

Consumers increasingly use and benefit from these services not only for directions, but also for other services like real-time traffic information, emergency assistance, or to help find the nearest restaurant or gas station. The market for such location-based services is expected to grow as companies make use of new technologies, such as those that integrate smart phones with vehicles and those that use crowd- sourced positioning, which uses location data gathered from a large number of consumers, to provide real-time traffic information.

According to one study, for example, the market for telematics services provided by auto manufacturers in North America is expected to increase from 11.8 million subscribers in 2012 to 31.6 million in 2016.[2]

As in-car location-based services have become commonplace, privacy groups and policy makers have questioned whether the location data collected and used by various companies in the course of providing such services pose privacy risks. Specifically, they are concerned that location data can be used for purposes other than to provide services to the consumer, such as selling the data to others for marketing. They also have concerns that location data can be used to track where consumers are, which can in turn be used to steal their identity, stalk them, or monitor them without their knowledge. In addition, location data can be used to infer other sensitive information about individuals such as their religious affiliation or political activities. Congress and several federal agencies have considered the implications of the collection of location data on consumer privacy. While legislative proposals aimed at protecting the privacy of location data by mobile devices and navigation systems have been introduced by Members of Congress, none of the proposals have been enacted.[3]

You asked us to review issues related to the privacy of location data collected by in-car location-based services. This report addresses (1) what selected companies that provide in-car location-based services use location data for, and if the companies share the data and (2) how these companies' policies and reported practices align with industry-recommended privacy practices.

This work complements a review that we conducted on the privacy of location data collected by mobile devices. In that review, we found that the companies in our sample did not consistently follow industry-recommended privacy practices and that federal agencies could clarify their expectations for steps companies should take to protect consumers' location data privacy. We recommended that the Federal Trade Commission (FTC) consider issuing guidance on protecting the privacy of location data and that the Department of Commerce's National Telecommunications and Information Administration (NTIA) outline goals, milestones, and performance measures for its ongoing process to develop industry codes of conduct.[4]

To address our objectives, we selected 10 companies that provide services that rely on the real-time transmission of location data from a device in the car to a central location. The 10 selected companies include six auto manufacturers, two PND companies, and two map and navigation application (app) developers for mobile devices.[5] While our findings are not generalizable to all companies that provide in-car location-based services, we selected auto manufacturers and PND companies that are the largest in the United States by market share and app developers that have widely used map and navigation apps on mobile devices. For example, the six auto manufacturers we selected constituted nearly 75 percent of new car sales in the United States in 2012. For each company, we examined documentation of the company's privacy practices in effect in 2013, which could include their privacy policies, terms of service agreements, and written disclosures to consumers, among other things. We further interviewed representatives from each of the companies to discuss its practices, as well as representatives from three third-party partners or contractors used by these companies to provide services, where applicable. While the 10 companies in our review may use a number of third-party companies to provide services, we selected three third-party companies to interview because they specifically provide telematics or traffic-information services. The findings from these third parties are not generalizable to all third parties that provide location-based services, but provided us with insights about third-party use of location data. We reviewed documents and interviewed officials from the FTC, which protects consumers against unfair or deceptive business practices, including privacy issues, and NTIA, which advises the President on telecommunications and information policy issues. We also interviewed privacy advocates and automobile industry associations for their views on privacy practices and potential privacy risks that consumers might experience if companies do not implement the practices. See appendix I for a more detailed description of our scope and methodology.

We conducted this performance audit from February 2013 to December 2013 in accordance with generally accepted government auditing standards. Those standards require that we plan and perform the audit to obtain sufficient, appropriate evidence to provide a reasonable basis for our findings and conclusions based on our audit objectives. We believe that the evidence obtained provides a reasonable basis for our findings and conclusions based on our audit objectives.

BACKGROUND

In-Car Location-Based Services

In-car location-based services are delivered by telematics systems, PNDs, and map and navigation apps for mobile devices. See figure 1 for a description and examples of these systems and devices.

Systems or devices that deliver in-car location-based services	Description	Examples
Telematics systems 	• Provided by auto manufacturers. • Consumers receive services through devices embedded in their cars or through their mobile devices that are connected to their cars.[a] • Services are generally subscription-based, requiring consumers to pay for services.	General Motors' OnStar, Ford Sync, Chrysler UConnect
Portable navigation devices (PND) 	• Provided by PND companies. • Consumers receive services through PNDs that are equipped to transmit location data, or through their mobile devices that are connected to their PNDs.[a] • Services can be free to consumers or require a fee for subscription.	TomTom, Garmin
Map and navigation applications for mobile devices 	• Provided by mobile application developers. • Consumers receive services through smart phones. • Services are generally free or relatively inexpensive.	Scout GPS Navigation, Google maps

Source: GAO analysis of telematics systems, PNDs, and map and navigation applications that provide in-car location-based services.

[a] In cases where mobile devices are used, consumers use wireless technology to connect their mobile devices to their cars or PNDs. Once connected, consumers can access certain mobile device location-based services on the devices embedded in their cars or on their PNDs.

Figure 1. Description and Examples of Systems or Devices That Deliver In-Car Location-Based Services to Consumers.

Telematics systems, PNDs, and map and navigation apps receive Global Positioning Satellite (GPS) signals, which identify the location of consumers in their cars.

The consumers' location data, which consist of GPS coordinates, are transmitted over the cellular network or Wi-Fi access points to companies providing the services. Based on the location information received, companies provide requested services to consumers. Companies may choose to partner with third parties to provide a specific location-based service, such as real-time traffic information.

Companies may also choose to contract with third-parties that provide all location-based services on their behalf; among our selected companies, this is most common among the auto manufacturers.[6] (See Figure 2.)

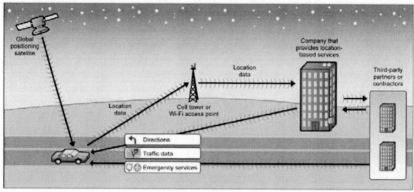

Source: GAO.

Note: While companies use cellular networks to transmit location data, we excluded telecommunications companies that provide these networks from this review because they were included in our 2012 report on mobile devices. See GAO-12-903.

Figure 2. How Location Data Are Transmitted to Provide In-Car Location-Based Services.

The in-car location-based services industry continues to change and evolve: new partnerships are emerging in the marketplace, existing companies are changing how they provide location-based services, and technologies are advancing. For example, in 2012, a telecommunications company—Sprint—announced that it would partner with Chrysler to provide location-based and other in-car communication services using wireless technology embedded in cars. To expand its presence in the telematics and connected-service market, SiriusXM Radio Inc., a satellite radio broadcasting company, announced in 2013 that it entered into an agreement to acquire Agero Connected Services Inc., a company that auto manufacturers contract with to provide location-based services. In addition, some market analysts state that the market for stand-alone PNDs is waning, and as a result, existing PND companies have established partnerships with auto manufacturers to provide navigation services embedded in cars and have developed apps for mobile devices. Furthermore, as technologies that provide location-based services advance, auto manufacturers look to improve driver experiences by making cars more connected to mobile devices.

Table 1. Industry-Developed Recommended Privacy Practices Applicable to Location Data

Category	Examples of specific practices
Disclosures to consumers about data collection, use, and sharing	• State reasons companies collect and share data. • State specifically that collection of location data is limited to specific needs. • Do not use data for a purpose other than what has been disclosed to consumers without providing notice and obtaining consent before using the data.
Controls over location data	• Obtain consumers' consent before collecting their personal information. • Provide consumers the ability to opt out of data collection to which they have previously consented. • Allow consumers to delete location data that have been collected.
Data safeguards and retention	• State a specific time frame for retaining consumer data. • Protect data with reasonable security safeguards against risks such as loss or unauthorized access.
Accountability	• Ensure employees protect consumers' data. • Keep third parties responsible for protecting consumers' data.

Source: GAO analysis of practices recommended by mobile industry associations and privacy advocacy organizations.

Industry Privacy Practices

Mobile industry associations and privacy advocacy organizations have recommended practices that companies can take to better protect consumers' privacy; we determined that these recommended practices can be applied to the companies discussed in this report.[7] Specific examples of recommended practices are shown in table 1.

Existing and Proposed Privacy Protections

Currently, no comprehensive federal privacy law governs the collection, use, and sale of personal information by private-sector companies; rather, the privacy of consumers' data is addressed in various federal laws. Some of these federal laws are relevant to location data (see table 2).[8] The privacy of consumers' location and other data is also protected in accordance with companies' privacy practices. Federal law does not require companies to notify consumers of their privacy practices, but companies within the scope of our review have conveyed these practices through privacy policies and other documents. Additionally, FTC has reported that because protecting privacy is important to consumers, companies that deal with consumer data, including location data, have placed emphasis and resources on maintaining reasonable security.

Table 2. Select Laws That Address Consumer Privacy and Their Relevance to Privacy of Location Data

Law	Description	Relevance to the privacy of location data
Federal Trade Commission (FTC) Act	This Act prohibits unfair or deceptive acts or practices in or affecting commerce and authorizes FTC enforcement action. This authority allows FTC to take remedial action against a company that engages in a practice that FTC has found is unfair or deceives its customers.	FTC could take action against a company if FTC found the company was being unfair or deceptive by not adhering to the company's own privacy policies that describe how location data are collected, used and shared.
The Communications Act of 1934 (Communications Act)	This Act, as amended, imposes a duty on telecommunications carriers to secure information and imposes particular requirements for protecting information identified as customer proprietary network information (CPNI), including the location of customers when they make calls. The Act also requires express authorization for access to or sharing of call location information concerning the user of commercial mobile services, subject to certain exceptions.	The Act covers location data collected by telecommunications carriers, not location data collected by companies that provide in-car location-based services.
Electronic Communications Privacy Act of 1986 (ECPA)	This Act prohibits the federal government and providers of electronic communications from accessing and sharing the content of consumers' electronic communications, unless approved by a court or by consumer consent. The Act also prohibits providers of electronic communications from voluntarily disclosing customer records to government entities, with certain exceptions, but companies may disclose such records to a person other than a governmental entity.	The Act does not specifically address whether location data are considered content or part of consumers' records. Some privacy groups have stated that ECPA should specifically address the protection of location data.

Source: GAO summary and analysis of select laws.

Some privacy groups, some Members of Congress, and others maintain that privacy rights are being compromised by new uses of technology that are not addressed in existing laws. In 2012, FTC and NTIA called on Congress to pass data privacy legislation that would provide a minimum level of protection for consumer data, including location data. Some Members of Congress have introduced bills that would address the privacy of consumers' electronic personal data, including location data. In particular, three of these bills would generally require commercial entities—such as those companies within the scope of this report—to provide notice and obtain consent from consumers to collect and share their location data.[9]

NTIA and FTC have both issued reports that offered recommendations aimed at improving overall consumer privacy, including location-based services. In February 2012, NTIA prepared a report for the White House that offered a framework and expectations for companies that use consumers' personal information, which includes location information.[10]

The framework includes a consumer privacy bill of rights that states that consumers are entitled to, among other things, exercise control over what personal information companies collect and how they use it, and to easily understand and access information about companies' data privacy and security practices. In March 2012, FTC issued a report that described recommended practices for companies that collect and use consumer data.[11] This report recommended, for example, that companies obtain affirmative express consent from consumers before collecting precise location data; limit collection to data needed for a requested service or transaction; and provide consumers with prominent notice about the sharing of their location data. Companies' use of NTIA's and FTC's practices for protecting consumers' data is voluntary. Like the industry-developed recommended location data privacy practices described in table 1, the recommendations offered by NTIA and FTC are consistent with the internationally recognized privacy practices called the Fair Information Practice Principles (FIPP).[12]

SELECTED COMPANIES STATED THAT THEY PRIMARILY COLLECT AND SHARE LOCATION DATA TO PROVIDE AND IMPROVE CONSUMER SERVICES

Representatives from all of the selected companies told us that they collect location data primarily to provide consumers with various requested location-based services. Telematics systems provided by the auto manufacturers we reviewed collect location data to respond to specific requests from consumers for location-based services such as turn-by-turn directions, information on local fuel prices, stolen vehicle tracking, or roadside assistance. Additionally, representatives from three auto manufacturers told us that their electric vehicle telematics systems use location data to help drivers of electric vehicles locate nearby charging stations. Separately, representatives from five auto manufacturers told us that their telematics systems also collect location data for other purposes. For example, a representative from one auto manufacturer told us that when a vehicle's diagnostic trouble code is displayed (e.g., the check engine indicator light is displayed) or during monthly checks by the telematics system, the company collects location data along with vehicle data to determine whether driving in certain locations, such as near power plants, affects a vehicle's overall performance. The companies we reviewed that sell PNDs and navigation apps for mobile devices similarly collect location data to provide consumers with requested traffic and navigation services. Some of these companies may also collect location data to provide consumers additional features such as the location of nearby restaurants or points of interest.

Representatives from all 10 selected companies told us that they share consumer location data with third parties to provide and improve services, with law enforcement, or with others for other purposes when data are de-identified.[13]

- Sharing to provide and improve services: Representatives from nine of the selected companies told us that they share location data to provide location-based services to consumers or to improve the accuracy of services provided to consumers; representatives from the remaining company said that it does not share location data of consumers using its traffic and navigation services because it provides these services in-house. The six selected auto manufacturers generally share location data with third parties that provide consumers with location-based services. For example, of these auto manufacturers, three authorize the same third-party contractor to collect and use vehicle-specific location data to provide telematics services on the auto manufacturers' behalf. Although the level of services varies by manufacturer, this third-party company provides services to consumers such as navigation assistance, traffic assistance, and concierge services where consumers can obtain assistance from live operators for business and personal needs such as making flight or restaurant reservations. Auto manufacturers' telematics systems may also share vehicle-specific location data with public-safety emergency-service providers and third-party roadside assistance providers so that they can provide emergency and breakdown assistance. Representatives from both PND companies and one app developer said that they share aggregated location data associated with traffic flows with third parties, including traffic information providers. Traffic information providers use such data, along with data from various other sources (such as traffic alerts and GPS data collected from vehicle fleets) to augment and improve the accuracy of real-time traffic services provided to consumers.

- Sharing with law enforcement: All 10 of the selected companies' disclosures describe circumstances under which they may share location data with law enforcement. For example, one company's disclosure states that the company can, when required, share location data "to comply with the law, in legal proceedings, to respond to subpoenas or court orders, and in cooperation with law enforcement agencies." Another company's disclosure states that it is not required to release any records that are created as part of its service without a subpoena (unless otherwise required by law). However, for companies that do not retain personally identifiable location data, there are no data for law enforcement to use.

- Sharing for other purposes: Representatives from two of the selected companies told us that they share location data for other purposes beyond providing services to consumers. Representatives from these two companies told us that they have provided location data that they have de-identified or aggregated to university research programs, the National Highway Transportation Safety Administration (NHTSA), and state departments of transportation for research purposes (e.g., causes of accidents) and to improve information about traffic patterns for infrastructure planning.[14] Representatives from both companies told us that they have contractual agreements in place with these entities that govern how the data should be used and protected. Separately, representatives from all of the selected companies told us that they do not share identifiable location data with or sell such data to marketing companies or data brokers that collect information for the purposes of reselling the information to others. However, representatives from one of these companies told us that it shares aggregated data with marketing companies.

As discussed in more detail below, while the companies we reviewed stated that they did not share data for purposes other than those mentioned, their policies give them the flexibility to do so. In addition, some companies do not describe the purposes for sharing de-identified location data in their disclosures to consumers. Furthermore, as we discuss later in this report, companies use various methods to de-identify location data, some of which could result in a consumer being re- identified (that is, their personally identifiable information could be reconstituted).

SELECTED COMPANIES HAVE IMPLEMENTED SOME RECOMMENDED PRACTICES, BUT THE EXTENT TO WHICH CONSUMERS' PRIVACY COULD BE AT RISK MAY NOT BE CLEAR

Industry-recommended practices state that companies should protect the privacy of location data by providing (1) disclosures to consumers about data collection, use, and sharing; (2) controls over location data; (3) data safeguards and explanations of retention practices; and (4) accountability for protecting consumers' data. The recommended practices are not required, but rather provide a framework for understanding the extent to which these companies protect the privacy of consumers' location data. We found that all 10 companies have taken steps that are consistent with some, but not all, of the recommended practices, and the extent to which consumers' data could be at risk may not be clear to consumers.

Selected Companies Disclose That They Collect and Share Location Data, but Disclosures to Consumers Are Sometimes Unclear

Recommended practices state that companies should clearly disclose how they collect, use, and share location data and the purposes for doing so. We found that companies use various methods to disclose their privacy practices, but the information about the use and sharing of location data was sometimes unclear. Without clear disclosures about the collection and sharing of location data, consumers may not be aware of all the purposes for which their data are collected and shared. Thus, data may be used and shared for purposes that the consumer is not expecting or to which the consumer might not have chosen to agree. Privacy advocates as well as the FTC and NTIA have stated that privacy disclosures should be clearly written, readily available, and describe all purposes for which personal data are collected and shared.

Notification Methods

All 10 selected companies use privacy policies, terms of service agreements, and other practices—such as on-screen notifications—to notify consumers of their privacy practices. Of the 10 companies we reviewed, six have stand-alone privacy policies and four use terms of service agreements that include an explanation of their privacy practices. Of the six companies that have stand-alone privacy policies, four companies and one of the auto manufacturers for its electric vehicle provide notice via an on-screen display. According to one auto manufacturer, its services are requested and provided through voice command and audible response rather than through a screen, making on- screen notifications impractical with current systems. Further, the nature of the service makes it difficult and inconvenient to notify consumers about location data collection each time service is requested. For example, the auto manufacturer said that it would not be practical for notification to occur in connection with the delivery of emergency services since those tend to be provided automatically, without consumer request, when there is an accident.

Purposes for Collection and Use

All 10 selected companies disclose the reasons for collecting location data, which are generally based on the types of services they provide. However, 9 of 10 companies also provide reasons for collecting location data that are broadly worded and potentially allow for unlimited data collection and use. For example, one company's terms of service states that the provided reasons for location data collection were not exhaustive. Furthermore, none of the selected companies explicitly state in their disclosures that location data are not collected for other purposes. Three of the selected companies state in their disclosures that they seek consumers' consent before using location data for purposes beyond those listed. Without clear disclosures about the purposes, consumers may not able to effectively judge whether the uses of their location data might violate their privacy. Furthermore, risks increase that data may be used for purposes the consumer is not expecting or to which the consumer might not have chosen to agree.

Purposes for Sharing Location Data

All 10 selected companies disclose that they share consumer location data with third parties, mainly to provide requested services. Six companies' disclosures allow for additional sharing for location data when they are de-identified, but the purposes for sharing such data were not described in five of these companies' disclosures. Although not disclosed, representatives from three of the five companies explained to us that they share de-identified or aggregate location data for providing services or for other purposes. Representatives from the remaining two companies said that although their disclosures give them the option to share de-identified location data, their companies do not share such location data at all. Because companies have not made clear disclosures about the purposes for sharing de-identified location data, risks increase that data may be used for purposes that the consumer is not expecting or to which a consumer might not have chosen to agree.

Selected Companies Obtain Consent and Provide Certain Controls for Collecting Location Data, but Consumers Are Not Able to Delete Their Collected Data

Recommended practices state that companies should obtain consumers' consent for collecting, using, and sharing personal information, including location data, and allow consumers to control their data, such as by opting-in and opting-out of collection and deleting location data. We found that companies obtain consumer consent and provide controls in a variety of ways, but do not allow consumers to request their historical location data to be deleted when data are associated with an individual or vehicle. Without the ability to delete their location data, consumers are unable to prevent the use or retention of their data, should they wish to do so. Privacy advocates, as well as the NTIA and FTC, have stated that consumers should provide their consent and have an appropriate level of control over how their personal data are collected, used, and shared. NTIA and privacy advocates have also stated that consumers should be able to request deletion of data collected about them.

Consent

The selected companies obtain consumer consent to collect location data in various ways, but some methods are more explicit than others. For example, auto manufacturers obtain consumer consent when consumers agree to the terms of service either when purchasing the vehicle equipped with the service or when signing-up and paying for the service. According to one privacy group we met with, if consent is obtained when a consumer purchases a vehicle, consumers may not be as likely to review a company's stated privacy practices because they may be a part of a larger set of documentation about the vehicle and its telematics system. Both PND companies and one auto manufacturer (for its electric vehicle) obtain consumer consent to collect location data more explicitly, via an on-screen prompt that allows consumers to accept or decline the transmission of such data. Both of the selected app developers we reviewed obtain consumer consent when consumers agree to the terms of the privacy policy or the terms of service (which includes a developer's privacy policy) when initially downloading the app.

Controls

The selected companies provide consumers various ways to opt in or out of location data collection. For example, auto manufacturers provide consumers with controls over location data collection by offering the telematics system as an option on a new vehicle purchase. However, auto manufacturers are including these systems as standard equipment on vehicles. In fact, one auto manufacturer told us it now provides a limited-time free subscription to its telematics service on most of its new cars, but that consumers can cancel at any time. According to the company, once a consumer cancels the subscription, location data are not collected, despite the equipment still being in the vehicle. Additionally, auto manufacturers told us that consumers can further choose to use these services or not. That is, a consumer has the option to request the location-based service and have location data transmitted, can refrain from using the service, or can cancel the service entirely. Both selected PND companies allow consumers to decide if they want their location data transmitted. For one PND company, consumers can opt in to the collection and sharing of location data for traffic information purposes via an on-screen prompt. Consumers who do not opt in will not receive traffic data but they can still use other location-based services, such as weather, if they choose to do so. For the other PND company, consumers can control the collection of all location data via an on-screen prompt or by adjusting the device's settings. If location data are turned off, consumers can still use the device for basic navigation but can no longer receive real-time traffic information. For the mobile device apps, consumers opt in to transmitting location data by downloading the app and requesting location-based services, and have the ability to opt out by not requesting services, changing the device's setting to prevent location data from being transmitted, or deleting the app entirely. When consumers download one particular app, the app asks whether it can collect anonymous location data at any time, including when not providing a specific navigation service. In this case, the default is to collect the anonymous location data unless the consumer takes an additional step to opt out. The app developer seeks to collect such data to improve its traffic-information and other services. The consumer can also adjust the device's settings at any time to prohibit the app from collecting the anonymous location data.

Deletion of Data

None of the 10 selected companies allow consumers to delete the location data that are, or have been, collected. Some companies de- identify and aggregate location data or do not retain any location data so it would not be possible for consumers to delete or request that their data be deleted. However, representatives from four companies told us that they keep the location data in a format that is associated with an individual vehicle yet do not allow consumers to delete their data or request their deletion. In such cases, consumers are unable to prevent the retention or use of retained data, should they wish to do so.

Selected Companies Stated That They De-Identify Location Data, but Different Methods and Retention Practices May Lead to Varying Levels of Protection for Consumers

Recommended practices state that companies should safeguard location data, in part, by de-identifying them; that companies should not keep location data longer than needed; and that such data should be deleted after a specific amount of time. We found that while selected companies safeguard location data in part by de-identifying them, companies use different de-identification methods that may lead to varying levels of protection for consumers. We also found wide variation in how long companies retain vehicle-specific or personally identifiable location data. Privacy groups we interviewed raised concerns about retaining location data for long periods of time because there are more opportunities to use the data to identify individuals or their behaviors and because longer retention periods put data at increased risk for unauthorized access or accidental disclosure. In addition, privacy groups said that de-identifying location data may not always protect consumers against privacy risks because some methods of de-identification can allow for an individual to be re-identified.

Safeguarding Location Data: De-Identification and Encryption

All of the selected companies stated in their disclosures, or in interviews with us, that they use or share de-identified location data. Representatives from some of the selected companies explained how they de-identify location data; the methods differed among the companies that responded, for example:

- A representative from one app developer told us that for its map and navigation application, the company does not associate location data with consumers, unless the consumers have signed into their accounts. In addition, this company uses other methods to further reduce the likelihood that individuals (who have not signed into their accounts) will be indentified, such as collecting location data periodically rather than continuously.

- Representatives from four companies told us that they de-identify location data by removing consumers' names from the location data, and associating the data with unique identification numbers. Three of these companies authorize their third-party contractor to collect location data along with a unique vehicle identification number or VIN that all vehicles possess. This third party associates the VIN with other information to determine which vehicle to provide location-based services to. Representatives from the fourth company told us that before they share data for research purposes, they associate location data with unique vehicle identifiers or aggregate them.

- Representatives from three companies told us that they de-identify location data they receive from consumers (after consumers provide their consent) by associating the location data with randomly generated identification numbers that change after a specific period of time.

- Representatives from three companies told us that before they share any location data with third parties, they strip the data of any identifiers and aggregate the data so that they are not tied to and not able to be tied to any particular consumer.

The de-identification method a company uses affects the extent to which consumers may be re-identified and exposed to privacy risks. Location data that are collected along with a consumer's name or other identifying information are, by definition, personally identifiable data and present the greatest privacy risks to consumers because a consumer's identity is known. Privacy risks decrease when companies de-identify location data, but the level of risk falls on a spectrum depending on how easy it is to re- identify consumers. De-identifying location data with unique identification numbers prevents the direct association of location data with a specific vehicle or individual. However, if the same identification number is re- used for the same consumer on multiple trips, then the consumer's history or patterns can potentially be discerned. In such instances, consumers face an increased likelihood that they can be re-identified. Privacy risks decrease if location data are associated with identification numbers that change over time because it is more difficult to discern an individual's history and identify an individual. Finally, consumers face little to no privacy risks when location data are stripped of any identification numbers and aggregated with other consumers' data because the data are anonymous, meaning that the data cannot be linked to an individual at all. (See Figure 3.) To the extent that companies use personally identifiable location data or use de-identification methods that allow a consumer to be re-identified, risks increase that consumer location data may be used in ways the consumer did not intend, such as to track their travel patterns or to target consumers for unwanted marketing solicitations.

Although location data that are coupled with personal information, such as a name, pose the greatest privacy risk to consumers, company representatives told us that in some cases, they need such data to provide certain services. For example, one auto manufacturer we met with said that one of its services—concierge services—is personalized to the consumer requesting the service and therefore relies on data that are associated with the individual requesting the services. Representatives from one third-party contractor that works with auto manufacturers said that consumers can receive a broader array of services by voluntarily providing additional data to service providers in connection with enrollment in the services. In contrast, representatives from PND companies and app developers told us that they do not need to know personally-identifiable information about a consumer to provide traffic and navigation services, just their location. As such, they said that their companies collect de-identified location data. In addition to de-identifying location data, all of the selected companies stated in their disclosures, or in interviews with us, that they safeguard location data or personal data that may include location data.

Eight companies' disclosures state that they implement physical, technical, or other safeguards and the remaining two told us they have these safeguards but did not state that they have them in any of their disclosures. Companies can safeguard location data by encrypting[15] them while they are being transmitted between a vehicle or device and the company that provides location-based services. In our analysis of data transmitted from two selected mobile apps to the developers who provide location-based services, we found that one developer encrypted all data transmitted from the app, so we could not discern what was being transmitted. The other developer did not encrypt the data transmission, and we were able to view the location data and other data, such as usernames and passwords, being transmitted. This developer acknowledged that such data were not encrypted and told us that it had made a decision independent from our review to encrypt the data in future releases of the app. To the extent that data are not encrypted, consumers may be at risk that their data may be subject to unauthorized access, disclosure, and modification.

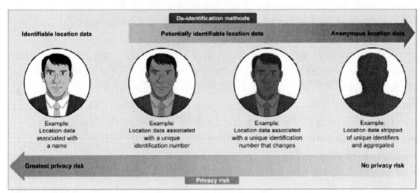

Source: GAO.

Figure 3. Examples of De-Identification Methods and Privacy Risk.

Retaining Location Data

None of the selected companies' disclosures discuss how long data are retained, but some company representatives we interviewed told us that that they do not retain location data "longer than necessary." A contractor that works with three companies in our review to provide location-based services told us that when a consumer requests services, in accordance with the contractual terms in place with the companies, the contractor may retain vehicle-specific location data, VIN, and other data associated with the consumer's request for up to 7 years. The contractor explained that it retains such subscriber information to protect against potential lawsuits, to allow the companies to evaluate how the contractor is performing, and for tax purposes should a tax authority audit their income associated with the provision of services. Representatives from one company stated that it retains personally identifiable location data for no more than 24 hours, and a representative from another company said that it does not retain such data at all. However, representatives from both of these companies told us that they retain de-identified location data indefinitely.[16] As we concluded in our 2012 report,[17] the longer identifiable location data are retained, the more vulnerable the data are to use by bad actors, such as hackers, or to unauthorized third-party access. Furthermore, risks increase that the amassed data could be used to create a detailed profile of individual behavior.

Selected Companies Have Taken Steps to Be Accountable for Protecting Location Data, but the Steps They Take within Their Companies Are Generally Not Disclosed to Consumers

Recommended practices state that companies should demonstrate accountability for their practices as well as the practices for third parties they use to provide services. If accountability practices are disclosed to consumers, then consumers may have greater assurance that their location data are reasonably protected. We found that most of the selected companies disclose to consumers that they hold third parties accountable for safeguarding data that are shared. However, none of the companies disclose to consumers how they hold themselves and their employees accountable to their privacy policies, although company representatives told us they are taking steps to ensure that they and their employees are protecting consumers' data and following their own privacy policies. Privacy groups and NTIA officials have stated that it is important for consumers to be assured that their location data are appropriately used and protected. To the extent that companies do not disclose the ways in which they hold themselves or third parties accountable, consumers will not be aware of how companies ensure that their data are appropriately protected.

Accountability with Third-Party Service Providers

All companies that share location data with third parties stated in their disclosures, or in interviews with us, that they take steps to protect location data that they share with third parties. For example, seven selected companies' disclosures or company representatives stated that third parties are contractually required to follow the companies' privacy policy or follow certain privacy practices. One of these companies has a business agreement with a third-party contractor that prohibits the contractor from collecting, using, and commingling data, including location data, about consumers or their behaviors for marketing purposes. In addition to holding third parties accountable through contracts, another company told us that in certain circumstances, it requires its third parties to conduct assessments to ensure that they are effectively protecting location data. Rather than conduct an assessment, some third parties choose to obtain certifications from professional security organizations. Separately, representatives from three companies told us that they protect location data that they share with third parties by de-identifying and aggregating them before they are shared.

Accountability within a Company

None of the companies stated in their disclosures how they hold themselves and their employees accountable for adhering to their privacy policies; however, company representatives we interviewed explained various ways in which they ensure that they and their employees are protecting consumers' data. Representatives from all of our selected companies told us that their employees must follow the companies' internal polices to protect data, including location data, and some of the representatives further explained that employees who violate such policies are subject to disciplinary action and possibly termination. Separately, representatives from one of the selected companies told us that it had conducted an independent audit of its practices to provide reasonable assurance that it was in line with company privacy policies. For example, to assess whether the company followed its policy to encrypt location data and make them anonymous, the independent auditor assessed whether the company encrypted location data in a way that only the company could decrypt and that location data were anonymous so that individuals could not be identified and tracked.[18] While companies are taking actions to ensure that they are protecting consumers' data, consumers may be unaware of these actions if they are not disclosed.

Our work provides information to policymakers on the various privacy risks consumers may face when companies collect and share location data to provide in-car location-based services. This information could be important to policymakers as they gauge whether privacy risks are appropriately balanced against the benefits that these services provide. Given that the report focuses on companies' privacy practices, we are not making recommendations to federal agencies at this time.

AGENCY COMMENTS

We provided drafts of this product to the Department of Commerce and FTC for comment. We also provided relevant portions of the draft to the 10 selected companies and three third-party companies for comment. We received technical clarifications from both federal agencies, all 10 of the selected companies, and two of the three selected third-party companies. We incorporated these technical clarifications as appropriate.

Sincerely yours,

Lori Rectanus
Acting Director, Physical Infrastructure

Table 3. Selected Companies That Provide In-Car Location-Based Services

Category	Company	Location-based service
Auto manufacturers	Chrysler	UConnect
	Ford	Sync
	General Motors	OnStar
	Honda	AcuraLink
	Nissan	Infiniti Connection, CARWINGS
	Toyota	Lexus Enform with Safety Connect, Toyota Entune
PND companies	Garmin	Traffic
	TomTom	LIVE Services
Map and navigation application developers[a]	Google Maps	Navigation function
	Telenav	ScoutGPS Navigation

Source: GAO.

[a] We also reviewed the policies and practices of Waze since it was one of the most popular apps, but during our review Waze was acquired by Google and was in the process of revising its policies and so declined to be interviewed for this report.

APPENDIX I: OBJECTIVES, SCOPE, AND METHODOLOGY

Our objectives were to examine (1) what selected companies that provide in-car location-based services use location data for and if they share it and (2) how these companies' policies and reported practices align with industry-recommended privacy practices. This work complements a review that we conducted on the privacy of location data collected by mobile devices.[19]

To address these objectives, we examined the privacy practices of companies that provide in-car location-based services. We focused on 10 companies that provide services that rely on the real-time transmission of location data from a car to a central location. These companies fall into three broad categories: (1) auto manufacturers, (2) portable navigation device (PND) companies,[20] and (3) map and navigation application (app) developers for mobile devices. We selected auto manufacturers and PND companies that are the largest in the United States by market share and app developers that have widely used map and navigation apps on mobile devices. See table 3. While our findings are not generalizable to all companies that provide in-car location-based services, the selected companies we reviewed are those that provide the most widely used services or represent a vast majority of the market. For example, the six auto manufacturers we selected represent nearly 75 percent of new car sales in the United States, and are therefore likely to have telematics systems that are more widely purchased by consumers.

We identified privacy practices for the 10 companies within the scope of our review by interviewing representatives from these companies and reviewing their privacy policies and other documentation that described their privacy practices in effect in 2013, such as terms of service agreements with consumers and agreements with third parties about how data should be used. We also interviewed representatives of and reviewed documents from third-party service providers that some of these companies use. In particular we interviewed representatives and reviewed documents from Agero Connected Services, Inc; Inrix; and HERE (a Nokia company). While the 10 companies in our review may use a number of third-party companies to provide services, we selected three third-party companies to interview because they specifically provide telematics or traffic-information services. The findings from these third parties are not generalizable to all third parties that provide location-based services, but provided us with insights about third-party use of location data.

To evaluate the 10 companies' privacy practices, we compared them to practices recommended by privacy advocates and groups representing the mobile industry. We identified the recommended practices in our 2012 report on mobile-device location data.[21] We determined that the recommended practices were applicable to companies providing in-car location-based services based on interviews with privacy advocacy groups and because our 2012 mobile device report found that the recommended practices generally aligned with the internationally recognized privacy practices called the Fair Information Practice Principles (FIPP).[22] To conduct the evaluation, two analysts conducted separate analyses of the 10 companies' privacy policies, other documentation on companies' privacy efforts, and information gained from our interviews to determine how the companies' practices compared to the recommended practices. Then, the two analysts obtained consensus on those determinations where there had not been agreement. In general, our evaluation examined the companies' privacy practices as stated in their privacy policies, other documentation, or in their interviews with us. We did not independently determine the extent to which companies implemented reported privacy practices, but we corroborated them with our own observations of these services and information from third parties where possible. For example, we were able to observe the actual practices that two selected mobile applications used to protect data transmitted from the applications to the developers. Specifically, we used a computer program to log, monitor, and document all network activity between the two mobile applications and the developers' servers.

To better understand companies' implementation of privacy practices and potential privacy risks[23] that consumers might experience if companies do not implement the practices, we met with a number of groups or individuals who are knowledgeable about the privacy of location data. Specifically, we met with privacy advocates (Future of Privacy Forum, Electronic Privacy Information Center, American Civil Liberties Union, Electronic Frontier Foundation, Center for Democracy and Technology); a company that certifies businesses privacy programs (TRUSTe); and one privacy researcher (Dorothy Glancy). We also met with associations knowledgeable about the automotive industry or in-car location-based technologies (Alliance of Automobile Manufacturers, Global Automakers, Center for Automotive Research, and the Intelligent Transportation Society of America) to better understand the direction of the automotive industry and technologies. Although the information provided by these groups, individuals, and associations are not generalizeable, their views provided us with a perspective on the benefits and risks associated with location data use and sharing. In addition, we reviewed documents and interviewed officials from Federal Trade Commission and the Department of Commerce's National Telecommunications and Information Administration. We also conducted a literature review on techniques to de-identify data.

We conducted this performance audit from February 2013 to December 2013 in accordance with generally accepted government auditing standards.

Those standards require that we plan and perform the audit to obtain sufficient, appropriate evidence to provide a reasonable basis for our findings and conclusions based on our audit objectives. We believe that the evidence obtained provides a reasonable basis for our findings and conclusions based on our audit objectives.

End Notes

[1] Telematics systems use telecommunication networks and GPS signals to allow information, such as location data, to be communicated between a car and a service provider.

[2] Frost & Sullivan, *Key Trends and Forecasts for the North American and Latin American Automotive Navigation and Telematics Services Market* (May 2012).

[3] See Geolocational Privacy and Surveillance Act, H.R. 1312, 113th Cong. (2013); Geolocational Privacy and Surveillance Act, S. 639, 113th Cong. (2013). Additionally, a bill was introduced in the 112th Congress that addressed the privacy of location data. See Location Privacy Protection Act of 2012, S. 1223, 112th Cong. (2011).

[4] GAO, *Mobile Device Location Data: Additional Federal Actions Could Help Protect Consumer Privacy,* GAO-12-903 (Washington, D.C.: Sept. 11, 2012). The report's recommendation to FTC has been implemented. NTIA did not agree with our recommendation.

[5] The selected auto manufacturers are Chrysler, Ford, General Motors, Honda, Nissan, and Toyota. The selected PND companies are Garmin and TomTom. The selected map and navigation application developers are Google Maps and Telenav. See appendix I for each of the companies' location-based services that we focused on for this review.

[6] Some PNDs and navigation systems in cars are not equipped to transmit location data in real time to companies. These devices and systems are able to provide navigation assistance based on satellite or other signals received. However, these types of devices and systems are not within the scope of our review because they pose less privacy risks to consumers as compared to devices and systems that transmit location data to companies.

[7] We identified the recommended practices for our 2012 review on mobile device location data. See GAO-12-903 for examples of the recommended practices. Appendix I of this report contains more information about how we determined that the recommended practices could be applied to companies discussed in this report.

[8] We reviewed select federal laws that are relevant to companies that provide in-car location-based services. We previously reported on a number of other federal privacy laws which were not relevant to our review. See GAO, *Information Resellers: Consumer Privacy Framework Needs to Reflect Changes in Technology and the Marketplace,* GAO-13-663 (Washington, D.C.: Sept. 25, 2013).

[9] See H.R. 1312, 113th Cong. (2013); S. 639, 113th Cong. (2013). Additionally, a bill was introduced in the 112th Congress that addressed the privacy of location data. See S. 1223, 112th Cong. (2011).

[10] The White House, *Consumer Data Privacy in a Networked World: A Framework for Protecting Privacy and Promoting Innovation in the Global Digital Economy* (Washington, D.C.: Feb. 23, 2012).

[11] Federal Trade Commission, *Protecting Consumer Privacy in an Era of Rapid Change: Recommendations for Businesses and Policymakers* (Washington, D.C.: March 2012).

[12] We used the industry-developed privacy practices—not the NTIA and FTC recommended practices—to evaluate our 10 selected companies' reported privacy practices because the industry-developed privacy practices are specific to location data. NTIA's and FTC's

recommended practices address consumer data, which include but are not specific to location data.

[13] "De-identified" location data are those data that have had personally identifiable information, such as a consumer's name or home address, removed or masked. When data are de-identified, a consumer's personally identifiable information could be reconstituted in certain circumstances (that is, the consumer can be re-identified). If location data are de-identified in a way that a consumer cannot be re-identified, then the data are anonymous. Aggregating de-identified data, which combines de-identified data from a number of individuals or vehicles, are anonymous because the data cannot be linked to an individual at all. Aggregated vehicle location data could be used, for example, to determine the speed of vehicles at 5 p.m. on a certain section of a road. The de- identification methods companies use may or may not result in location data that are anonymous. For more information on de-identified, anonymous, and aggregated data, see National Institute of Standards and Technology, *Guide to Protecting the Confidentiality of Personally Identifiable Information (PII)*, Special Publication 800-122 (Gaithersburg, Maryland: April 2010).

[14] Specifically, representatives from one company told us that it shares location data that are associated with unique vehicle identifiers or location data that are aggregated. The other company shares location data that have been de-identified and aggregated.

[15] Encryption protects data through a process of transforming ordinary data (commonly referred to as plaintext) into code form (ciphertext) so that the data are unintelligible to users without the proper decryption key.

[16] Representatives from one of the companies told us that the data it retains are aggregated location data, and representatives from the other company told us that the data it retains are location data associated with unique identification numbers that change.

[17] GAO-12-903.

[18] The audit determined that the company effectively encrypted and de-identified the location data.

[19] GAO-12-903.

[20] Some PNDs only receive GPS satellite signals and are not equipped to transmit location data to companies. These types of devices are not within the scope of our study because they do not transmit location data in real-time.

[21] GAO-12-903.

[22] The FIPPs are widely accepted principles for protecting the privacy and security of personal information. They were first proposed in 1973 by a U.S. government advisory committee. FIPPs are not precise legal requirements. Rather, they provide a framework of principles for balancing the need for privacy with other interests. The Organisation for Economic Co-operation and Development (OECD), an international organization, developed a revised version of the FIPPs in 1980 that has been widely adopted. See GAO-12-903 for more information.

[23] This review was not designed to identify whether there were any actual violations of consumers' privacy.

INDEX

A

access, vii, viii, 1, 4, 7, 10, 11, 12, 14, 16, 19, 20, 21, 22, 23, 24, 25, 27, 30, 39, 41, 43, 44, 47, 49, 50, 51, 59, 61, 62
accountability, 26, 54, 62
adults, 35, 37
advertisements, 25
advocacy, 8, 49, 65
age, 25
agencies, 3, 5, 26, 29, 42, 45, 53, 63, 64
American Civil Liberties Union, 30, 66
assessment, 63
assets, 36
AT&T, 17, 21, 30, 33, 36, 37, 38
audit, 46, 62, 63, 66, 68
authority(s), 26, 27, 28, 50, 62
auto manufacturers, viii, 41, 42, 44, 45, 47, 48, 52, 55, 57, 60, 65, 67
Automobile, 66
awareness, 3, 13, 19

B

base, 8, 9
behaviors, 59, 63
benefits, 6, 8, 13, 14, 19, 29, 30, 63, 66
blogs, 35
breakdown, 53
browser, 9

business environment, 11, 12, 17, 20
business model, vii, 1
businesses, 7, 10, 66

C

cable system, 34
cable television, 4
CAN-SPAM Act, 6
Capitol Hill, 28
caregivers, 7
category a, 7
challenges, viii, 2, 3, 6, 10, 13, 14, 17, 20, 29, 30, 37
Chamber of Commerce, 5
children, 5, 7, 8, 13, 19, 22, 25, 28, 33
Clinton Administration, 13
codes, 25, 26, 45
codes of conduct, 25, 26, 45
coffee, 9
collaboration, viii, 2, 26, 29
commerce, 34, 50
commercial, 5, 6, 9, 24, 28, 34, 50, 51
commercial email, 6
common carriers, 27
communication, viii, 26, 41, 44, 48
communication systems, viii, 41, 44
Communications Act, 4, 27, 43, 50
Communications Act of 1934, 4, 43, 50
competition, 17, 33, 37

compliance, viii, 2, 14, 24, 26, 30, 38
comprehension, 24
computer, 7, 24, 66
confidentiality, 3
configuration, 34
Congress, 3, 26, 29, 45, 51, 67
connectivity, vii, 1
consensus, 10, 17, 66
consent, 16, 17, 18, 19, 24, 25, 26, 37, 43,
    49, 50, 51, 55, 56, 57, 59
Constitution, 34, 39
consumer choice, 3, 17, 19, 20, 24
consumer education, 13
consumer protection, 25
cooperation, 53
counsel, 20
CT, 26
customer relations, 17, 25, 34
customers, 7, 10, 15, 17, 19, 21, 34, 37, 50
CV, 39
cybersecurity, 5, 34

D

danger, 25
data brokers, viii, 41, 42, 53
data collection, 18, 43, 49, 54, 55, 57
deficiencies, 12
dementia, 7
democrats, 34
Department of Commerce, 3, 5, 15, 25, 26,
    42, 45, 64, 66
Department of Homeland Security, 15
Department of Justice, 6
destruction, 22, 39
disclosure, 4, 10, 11, 12, 16, 18, 20, 22, 29,
    30, 39, 53, 59, 61
distress, 12
DOC, 34
dogs, 7
draft, 64
drawing, viii, 2

E

economic development, 14
ECPA, 34, 39, 43, 50
education, 5, 13
educational materials, 5
electronic communications, 28, 50
Electronic Communications Privacy Act, 43
e-mail, 5
emergency, 8, 44, 53, 55
emergency response, 8
employees, 24, 43, 49, 62, 63
encryption, 5
end-users, 16
enforcement, 4, 25, 26, 27, 28, 50, 53
enrollment, 60
entrepreneurs, 3
environment, 13
equipment, 57
European Parliament, 39
evidence, 46, 67
evolution, 20
exercise, 17, 19, 51
expertise, 6

F

Facebook, 10, 32, 35, 36, 37
FCC, viii, 2, 3, 4, 5, 6, 8, 15, 18, 20, 27, 33,
    34, 35, 36, 37, 38, 39
Federal Communications Commission, viii,
    2, 31, 32, 34
federal government, 11, 26, 37, 50
federal law, 49, 67
fleet tracking, vii, 1
flexibility, 54
flight, 53
force, 5
Ford, 64, 67
foreclosure, 7
fraud, 24
fuel prices, 52

G

GAO, ix, 41, 42, 43, 47, 48, 49, 50, 61, 64, 67, 68
General Motors, 64, 67
geolocation, 20, 37
GPS, 7, 9, 21, 44, 47, 53, 67, 68
growth, 6, 19, 35
guidance, 3, 15, 45
guidelines, 11, 20, 21, 38

H

handheld devices, 9
history, 60
host, viii, 2
hotel(s), 7, 9
hotspots, 9
House, 26, 27, 28, 37, 38
House of Representatives, 26, 27, 37, 38
HUD, 35

I

ID, 8
ideals, 3
identification, 43, 44, 58, 59, 60, 68
identity, 5, 23, 45, 60
income, 62
individuals, 16, 22, 27, 38, 39, 45, 59, 63, 66, 68
industry, vii, viii, ix, 2, 3, 4, 5, 6, 8, 10, 11, 12, 13, 14, 15, 17, 18, 19, 22, 25, 26, 29, 30, 32, 38, 41, 42, 45, 46, 48, 49, 51, 64, 65, 66, 67
infrastructure, 53
integrity, 22, 23
interface, 14, 38
interference, 18
intermediaries, 18
inventory management, vii, 1
issues, viii, 2, 3, 4, 5, 6, 12, 13, 14, 20, 21, 23, 24, 25, 26, 28, 29, 30, 38, 45, 46

J

job creation, 14
judiciary, 34, 36
Judiciary Committee, 26

L

Latin America, 67
law enforcement, 4, 22, 52, 53
laws, 5, 12, 13, 49, 50, 51, 67
LBS, vii, viii, 1, 2, 3, 6, 7, 8, 9, 10, 11, 12, 13, 14, 15, 16, 17, 18, 19, 20, 21, 22, 26, 29, 30, 36, 38
lead, 13, 14, 58
leadership, 26
legislation, 11, 25, 26, 27, 51
legislative proposals, 45
light, viii, 2, 52
location data, vii, viii, ix, 3, 9, 12, 16, 18, 19, 20, 22, 24, 27, 28, 38, 41, 42, 43, 44, 45, 47, 48, 49, 50, 51, 52, 53, 54, 55, 56, 57, 58, 59, 60, 61, 62, 63, 64, 65, 66, 67, 68
location information, 3, 7, 10, 12, 15, 16, 17, 18, 19, 21, 22, 26, 36, 38, 47, 50, 51
location-based services, vii, viii, ix, 1, 6, 17, 19, 20, 29, 35, 41, 42, 44, 45, 46, 47, 48, 50, 51, 52, 57, 59, 61, 63, 64, 65, 67
loyalty, 7, 10

M

majority, 9, 10, 17, 65
management, vii, 1, 7, 35
MapQuest, 35
market share, ix, 42, 45, 65
marketing, 13, 16, 19, 37, 42, 45, 53, 60, 63
marketplace, 10, 14, 48
Maryland, 8, 35, 68
McCain, John, 27
McCain, Senator John, 27
messages, 6
methodology, 46

Microsoft, 16, 19, 20, 21, 33, 36, 37, 38
misuse, 6, 29
MMA, 16, 19, 22, 37, 38, 39
mobile device, viii, 2, 8, 10, 12, 13, 14, 16, 26, 27, 33, 36, 37, 39, 42, 45, 46, 47, 48, 52, 58, 65, 67
mobile phone, 15

N

navigation system, 45, 67
networking, 10
non-governmental entities, 28
North America, 44, 67
NPR, 35

O

OECD, 44, 68
Office of Management and Budget, 13
officials, 46, 62, 66
operating system, 9, 10, 15, 20, 21
operations, 24
opportunities, viii, 3, 13, 14, 41, 44, 59
opt out, 27, 30, 49, 58
organize, vii, 2, 29
outreach, 13, 24

P

parental consent, 25
parents, 7, 8, 13, 19, 33
participants, 22, 36
password, 23
penalties, 27
permission, 6, 10, 11, 12, 21
personally identifiable data, vii, 1, 60
platform, 12
PNDs, viii, 41, 46, 47, 48, 52, 67, 68
police, 7
policy, viii, 3, 5, 8, 14, 15, 17, 20, 21, 23, 37, 41, 45, 46, 57, 63
policy issues, 46
policy makers, viii, 41, 45

policymakers, 63
potential benefits, 14
power plants, 52
President, 36, 37, 38, 46
prevention, 24
principles, 11, 15, 24, 25, 68
Privacy Protection Act, 13, 26, 28, 39, 67
product design, 30
proliferation, 26
protection, 3, 4, 22, 25, 28, 39, 50, 51, 58
public education, 8
public safety, 7, 12
publishing, 37

R

radio, 7, 48
radius, 8
real estate, 7, 15, 35
real time, 18, 67
recommendations, 25, 42, 51, 63
Reform, 34, 39
regulations, 6
rent, 7
requirements, viii, 2, 4, 22, 28, 30, 38, 50, 68
resolution, 8
resources, 11, 20, 37, 50
response, 11, 55
responsiveness, viii, 2, 29
restaurants, 7, 52
retail, 27, 35
rewards, 10
rights, 3, 4, 15, 30, 51
risk(s), 8, 14, 15, 22, 23, 39, 42, 43, 45, 46, 49, 54, 55, 56, 59, 60, 61, 62, 63, 66, 67
rules, 4, 6, 11, 20, 28, 29, 39

S

safety, 35, 53
scope, 25, 28, 46, 50, 51, 65, 67, 68
security, 3, 4, 5, 8, 14, 20, 21, 22, 23, 25, 26, 27, 28, 29, 39, 49, 50, 51, 63, 68

security practices, 14, 25, 51
Senate, 26, 27, 28, 44
sensitivity, 22, 24, 25
servers, 66
service provider, 9, 28, 53, 60, 65, 67
services, vii, viii, ix, 1, 3, 6, 14, 15, 16, 17,
    18, 19, 20, 22, 23, 24, 29, 35, 37, 38, 41,
    42, 44, 45, 46, 47, 48, 50, 51, 52, 53, 55,
    56, 57, 59, 60, 61, 62, 63, 64, 65, 67
showing, 5
signals, 47, 67, 68
silver, 10
small businesses, 5, 34
smart phones, viii, 41, 44
social network, vii, 1, 6, 7, 10, 17
solution, 6
Sprint, 32, 36, 48
stakeholders, 24, 25, 26
state(s), 19, 48, 51, 53, 54, 55, 56, 58, 61,
    62
statutes, 3
storage, 22
subpoena, 53
subscribers, 4, 34, 44
suppliers, 21

T

target, 60
Task Force, 36
technical comments, 42
techniques, 16, 66
technology(s), vii, 1, 3, 6, 8, 9, 14, 19, 27,
    29, 30, 35, 36, 48, 51, 66
telecommunications, 4, 5, 8, 34, 46, 48, 50
Telecommunications Act, 34, 36
telematics systems, viii, 41, 46, 47, 52, 53,
    65
telephone, 4, 34
tension, 18
theft, 5, 27

threats, 29
time frame, 30, 49
Toyota, 64, 67
trade, 5, 11, 16, 27
traffic information, vii, 1, 42, 44, 47, 53, 57
training, 24
transmission, 23, 39, 45, 57, 61, 65
transparency, 6, 14, 15, 16, 17, 19, 25, 30
transportation, 53
treatment, 4

U

uniform, 18
United, v, vii, 1, 41, 44, 45, 65
United States, v, vii, 1, 41, 44, 45, 65
USA, 35
user profile, viii, 2

V

vehicles, 44, 52, 57, 59, 68
Verizon, 17, 21, 31, 36, 37, 38
Vice President, 33, 36, 37, 38
videos, 7

W

Washington, 67
web, 7, 25, 38
web browser, 7
White House, 5, 51, 67
White Paper, 37, 38, 39
Wi-Fi, 9, 34, 47
windows, 7
wireless devices, 7
wireless technology, 47, 48
worldwide, 6, 20